The MAILBOX

The Education Center

Math
Practice Galore

Skill-Based Puzzle Pages

- Addition
- Subtraction
- Multiplication
- Division
- Fractions
- Decimals

Managing Editor: Amy Payne

Editorial Team: Becky S. Andrews, Kimberley Bruck, Sharon Murphy, Debra Liverman, Diane Badden, Thad H. McLaurin, Peggy Hambright, Karen A. Brudnak, Jennifer Nunn, Hope Rodgers, Dorothy C. McKinney, Melissa Hauck Bryan, Colleen Dabney, Terry Healy, John Hughes, Heather Kime Markland

Production Team: Lori Z. Henry, Pam Crane, Rebecca Saunders, Chris Curry, Sarah Foreman, Theresa Lewis Goode, Greg D. Rieves, Eliseo De Jesus Santos II, Barry Slate, Donna K. Teal, Zane Williard, Kitty Campbell, Tazmen Carlisle, Kathy Coop, Marsha Heim, Lynette Dickerson, Mark Rainey, Amy Kirtley-Hill

Fun, independent skill practice!

D1511829

www.themailbox.com

Manufactured in the United States
10 9 8 7 6 5 4 3 2 1

Table of Contents

Fractions

Decimals

● Aloha! ●

Begin at Start. Connect each number in order from least to greatest to reveal the picture.

225,500

275,000

125,500

105,600

279,500

370,000

407,000

450,000

645,386

654,250

672,500

672,930

645,400

673,250

680,500

679,999

710,000

757,286

674,750

925,090

861,000

860,231

775,286

998,999

952,090

801,999

75,600

999,999

Finish

44,772

29,333

42,427

30,333

44,727

28,001

21

99

21,800

15

102

Start

7

12,999

123

231

324

1,324

12,987

12,998

• Around the Park •

Write the value of six in each number. Then record your answer in the grid. The last letter of each answer will be the first letter of the next answer. The first one has been started for you.

A									B						
S	i	x	m	i											

A. 6,451,324

    six millions _____

B. 7,645,812

_____

C. 6,721,519

_____

D. 5,321,069

_____

E. 4,337,561

_____

F. 9,051,649

_____

G. 7,436,495

_____

• Xs and Os •

Add. If the answer on the grid is correct, mark it with an X. If the answer is incorrect, mark it with an O. The winner will have four in a row.

A.   4,325
    + 897
	B. 1,947
	    + 535
		C. 6,518
		    + 794
			D. 8,756
			    + 648

E.   9,375
    + 347
	F. 3,659
	    + 948
		G. 1,753
		    + 547
			H. 6,847
			    + 683

I.   8,955
    + 786
	J. 9,749
	    + 485
		K. 2,665
		    + 195
			L. 4,593
			    + 787

B. 2,284	K. 2,860	J. 14,302	C. 1,237
F. 4,607	E. 7,922	I. 9,741	H. 3,075
A. 5,222	L. 5,380	G. 2,300	D. 9,404

•Tied in Knots•

Add. Then draw a line to connect each matching answer.

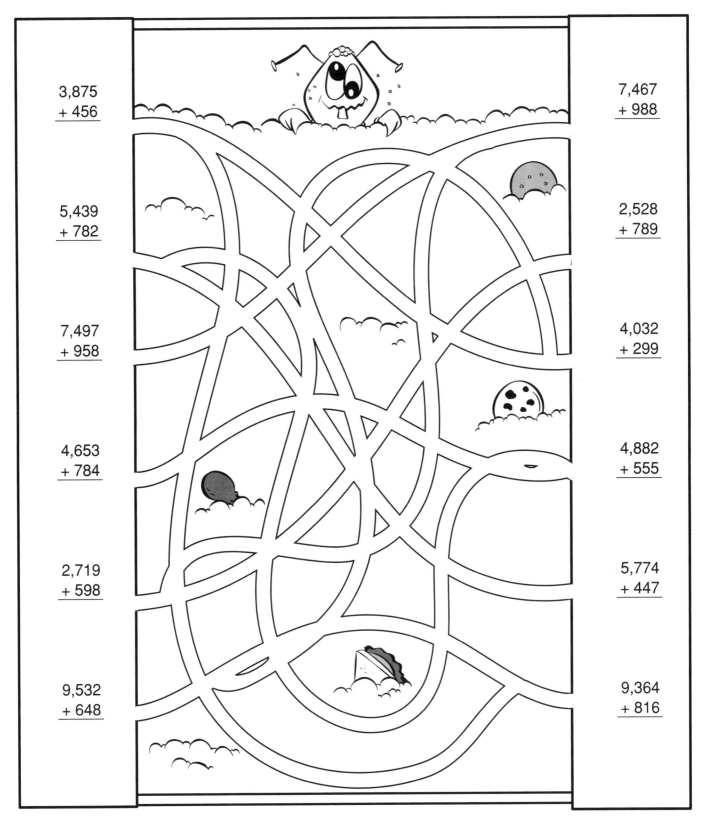

3,875
+ 456

5,439
+ 782

7,497
+ 958

4,653
+ 784

2,719
+ 598

9,532
+ 648

7,467
+ 988

2,528
+ 789

4,032
+ 299

4,882
+ 555

5,774
+ 447

9,364
+ 816

• Shaken Up! •

Use the code to find the value of each symbol. Then add.

A. ☐,☐☐☐   5,626
   + ☐☐☐   + 394

F. ☐,☐☐☐
   + ☐,☐☐☐

H. ☐,☐☐☐
   + ☐,☐☐☐

E. ☐,☐☐☐
   + ☐,☐☐☐

I. ☐,☐☐☐
   + ☐,☐☐☐

B. ☐,☐☐☐
   + ☐,☐☐☐

G. ☐,☐☐☐
   + ☐,☐☐☐

D. ☐,☐☐☐
   + ☐,☐☐☐

J. ☐,☐☐☐
   + ☐,☐☐☐

C. ☐,☐☐☐
   + ☐,☐☐☐

Code

1	2	3
4	5	6
7	8	9

Record each answer in the chart below. If completed correctly, the numbers will appear in order from least to greatest.

__,__ 0	6,___	__,6 __	__,_1_	0,___
A	B	C	D	E

1_,___	__,9__	3,___	__,_2_	__,__1
F	G	H	I	J

•From the Ground Up•

Add. Then record each sum in the puzzle.

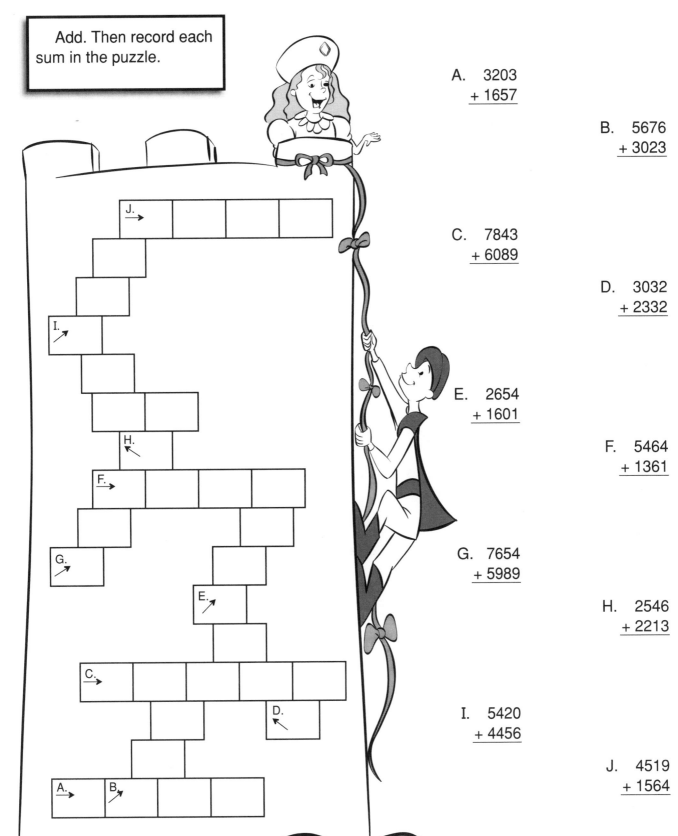

A. 3203
  + 1657

B. 5676
  + 3023

C. 7843
  + 6089

D. 3032
  + 2332

E. 2654
  + 1601

F. 5464
  + 1361

G. 7654
  + 5989

H. 2546
  + 2213

I. 5420
  + 4456

J. 4519
  + 1564

Just Cruising Along

Subtract. Write the answer in the puzzle.

Across

A. 7,325 − 641 =

C. 9,632 − 883 =

D. 9,424 − 635 =

F. 2,533 − 287 =

I. 4,312 − 567 =

Down

B. 5,734 − 886 =

C. 9,245 − 757 =

E. 8,532 − 957 =

G. 9,841 − 562 =

H. 5,230 − 394 =

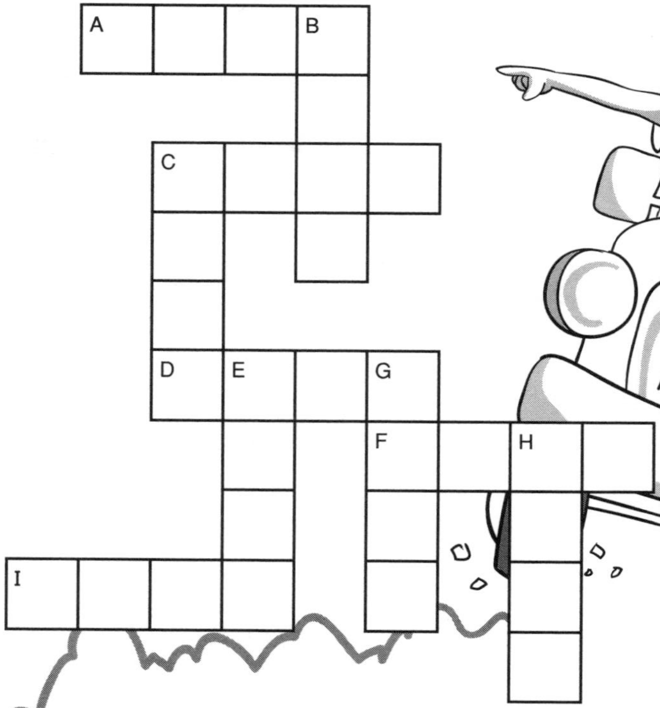

• Shoreline Greeting •

Subtract. Then follow the directions on the treasure chest. Write the remaining words in order to answer the question.

A. 7,321 – 752 HIGH	B. 6,254 – 365 OCEAN	C. 5,842 – 955 LONG	D. 7,482 – 3,594 TIME
E. 3,457 – 678 MOON	F. 4,253 – 895 NO	G. 3,126 – 389 LOW	H. 7,571 – 789 IS
I. 6,362 – 578 OUT	J. 5,213 – 894 SEA	K. 3,528 – 719 BOAT	L. 4,726 – 3,637 FUN

What did the beach say when the tide came in?

_____ _____ _____ "_____"!

Welcome!

Cross out all answers that
• have a 2 or a 4 in the ones place
• contain both a 5 and a 9
• contain two 7s
• contain a 0

Seek and Find!

Subtract. Circle each answer in the puzzle.

A. 4,003
   − 675

B. 2,008
   − 499

C. 6,070
   − 985

D. 3,009
   − 725

E. 1,007
   − 528

F. 3,400
   − 872

G. 9,005
   − 366

H. 7,400
   − 273

I. 2,050
   − 923

J. 4,060
   − 864

K. 7,008
   − 536

L. 3,001
   − 625

1	3	5	6	7	5	3	2	2	8	4
1	5	0	9	2	1	2	5	1	9	7
2	0	7	6	3	7	1	2	5	2	4
7	8	8	9	4	4	5	8	6	3	9
2	5	4	4	3	7	7	1	2	7	5
1	3	3	2	8	8	2	9	2	6	3
4	6	3	1	9	6	9	0	4	3	2

• Magic Pizza •

Subtract. If you are correct, the sum of the answers in each row, column, and diagonal will be the same.

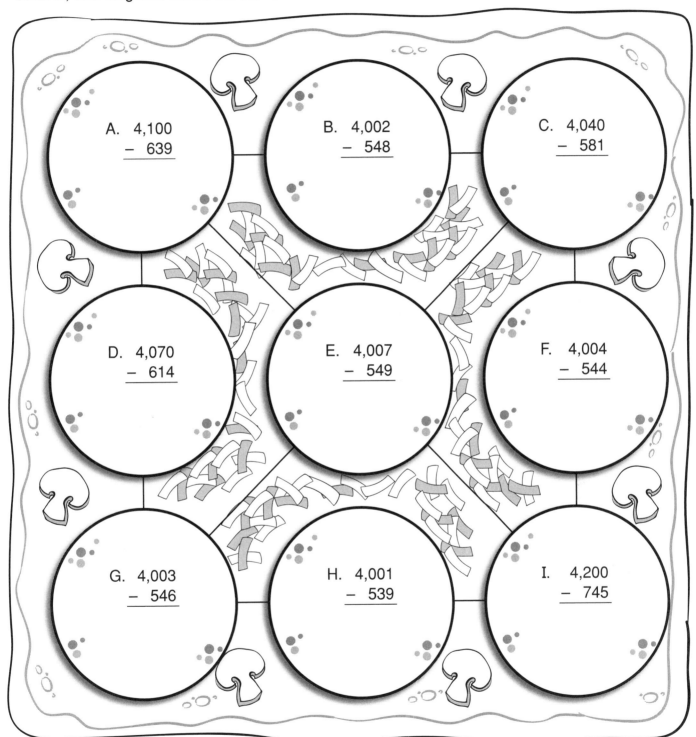

A. 4,100
  − 639

B. 4,002
  − 548

C. 4,040
  − 581

D. 4,070
  − 614

E. 4,007
  − 549

F. 4,004
  − 544

G. 4,003
  − 546

H. 4,001
  − 539

I. 4,200
  − 745

What is the sum of the answers in each row, column, and diagonal?

_____

• Fairway Fun •

How old was Tiger Woods when he won his first tournament?

Multiply. Then connect the golf balls next to the odd-numbered products in order from least to greatest to answer the question.

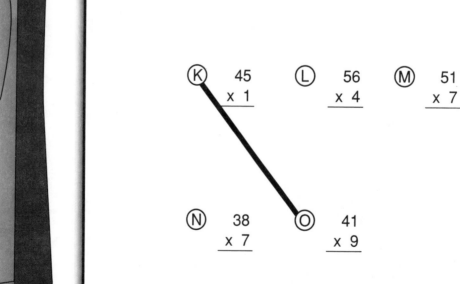

Ⓐ 62
   x 8

Ⓑ 49
   x 3

Ⓒ 17
   x 9

Ⓓ 53
   x 6

Ⓔ 17
   x 7

Ⓕ 36
   x 5

Ⓖ 19
   x 6

Ⓗ 21
   x 3

Ⓘ 66
   x 3

Ⓙ 78
   x 7

Ⓚ 45
   x 1

Ⓛ 56
   x 4

Ⓜ 51
   x 7

Ⓝ 38
   x 7

Ⓞ 41
   x 9

• What's Making the Noise? •

Multiply. Cut out the answer boxes. Glue each box to its matching space in the grid to create a picture.

41 x 2	71 x 3	20 x 5	11 x 6	24 x 7
22 x 4	16 x 4	25 x 6	83 x 7	50 x 8
81 x 6	37 x 5	29 x 5	18 x 4	94 x 3
19 x 9	32 x 3	90 x 6	68 x 4	11 x 9
55 x 3	44 x 8	89 x 2	62 x 7	13 x 9

282	99	168	400	213	64	82	117	540
165	88	486	185	145	96	66	72	
150	171	100	352	178	272	581	434	

• The Mail Trail •

Multiply. Write each product in the grid. The last digit of each answer is the first digit of the next answer.

A. 127
  x 4

B. 416
  x 2

C. 504
  x 4

D. 707
  x 9

E. 545
  x 7

F. 734
  x 8

G. 493
  x 5

H. 834
  x 6

I. 685
  x 7

J. 732
  x 8

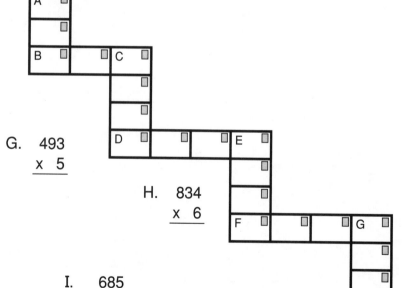

• Catching Butterflies •

Use the code to multiply. Cross off the products on the butterflies.
The sum of the remaining numbers should equal 5,000.

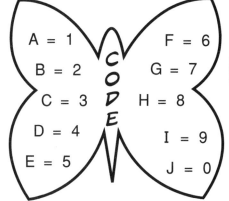

CODE

A = 1	F = 6
B = 2	G = 7
C = 3	H = 8
D = 4	I = 9
E = 5	J = 0

4,040

3,368

1,585

876

1,326

5,800

1,325

1,887

784

1,632

2,541

6,840

2,958

1,432

1. DCH x B	2. AIF x D	3. GBE x H	4. BBA x F
5. FBI x C	6. GFJ x I	7. BFE x E	8. CEH x D
9. DIC x F	10. CAG x E	11. CFC x G	12. EJE x H

"A-maze-ing" Pyramid

Multiply. Then, beginning at Start, find the path from one product to the next greater product.

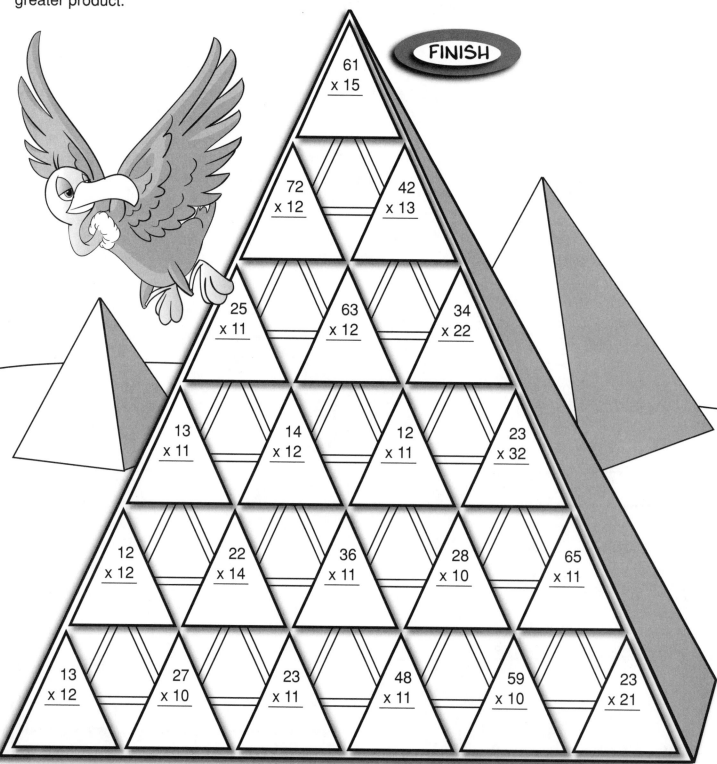

FINISH

61
x 15

72   42
x 12   x 13

25   63   34
x 11   x 12   x 22

13   14   12   23
x 11   x 12   x 11   x 32

12   22   36   28   65
x 12   x 14   x 11   x 10   x 11

13   27   23   48   59   23
x 12   x 10   x 11   x 11   x 10   x 21

START

• Digging for Treasure •

Multiply. Write your answers in the puzzle. Then add the answers together to see whether you found all the gems.

The total number of gems is 22,320.

• How High Can You Climb? •

Multiply the problem on the lowest step in each set. Write the last two digits of the answer as the first number of the next problem. Continue to the top.

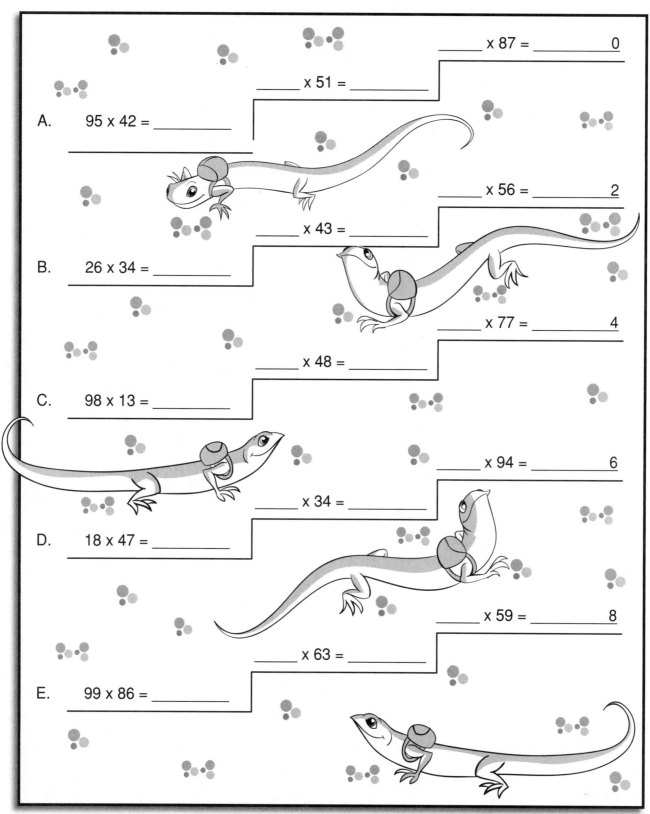

_____ x 87 = _____ 0

_____ x 51 = _____

A.   95 x 42 = _____

_____

_____ x 56 = _____ 2

_____ x 43 = _____

B.   26 x 34 = _____

_____ x 77 = _____ 4

_____ x 48 = _____

C.   98 x 13 = _____

_____ x 94 = _____ 6

_____ x 34 = _____

D.   18 x 47 = _____

_____ x 59 = _____ 8

_____ x 63 = _____

E.   99 x 86 = _____

• Spoiling the Picnic •

Multiply. Write the first two digits of the answer as the first number of the next problem. Continue to the end of the maze. When you reach the picnic basket, your product should be the number on the basket.

Start

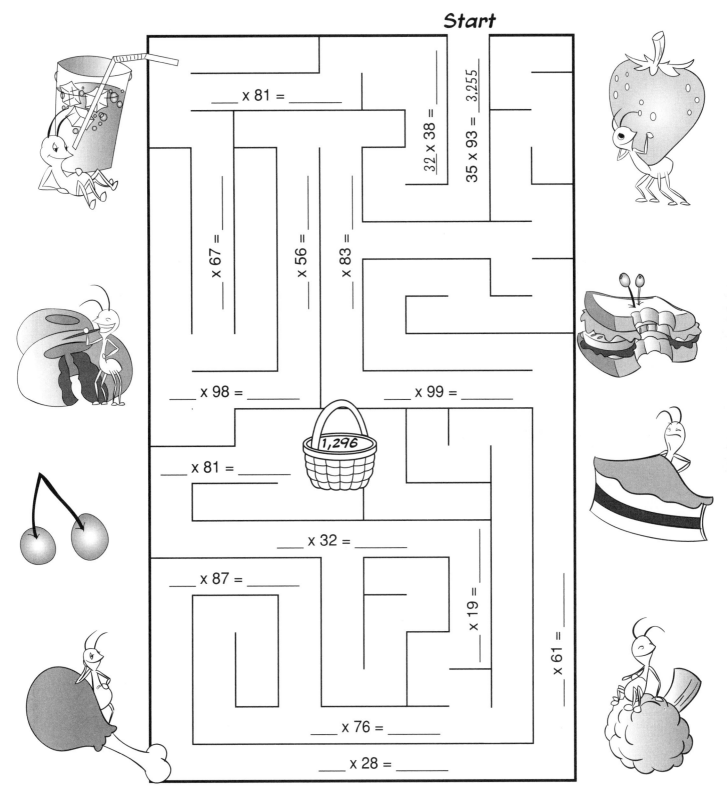

_____ x 81 = _____

$\underline{32}$ x 38 = _____

35 x 93 = $\underline{3,255}$

_____ x 67 = _____

_____ x 56 = _____

_____ x 83 = _____

_____ x 98 = _____   _____ x 99 = _____

1,296

_____ x 81 = _____

_____ x 32 = _____

_____ x 87 = _____

_____ x 19 = _____

_____ x 61 = _____

_____ x 76 = _____

_____ x 28 = _____

• What's for Dessert? •

Multiply. Circle each product below. Then connect the dots by the circled answers in order from least to greatest.

A. 23
  x 13

B. 87
  x 27

C. 63
  x 29

D. 97
  x 48

E. 92
  x 13

F. 78
  x 60

G. 56
  x 54

H. 97
  x 83

I. 91
  x 15

J. 78
  x 46

K. 56
  x 44

L. 69
  x 14

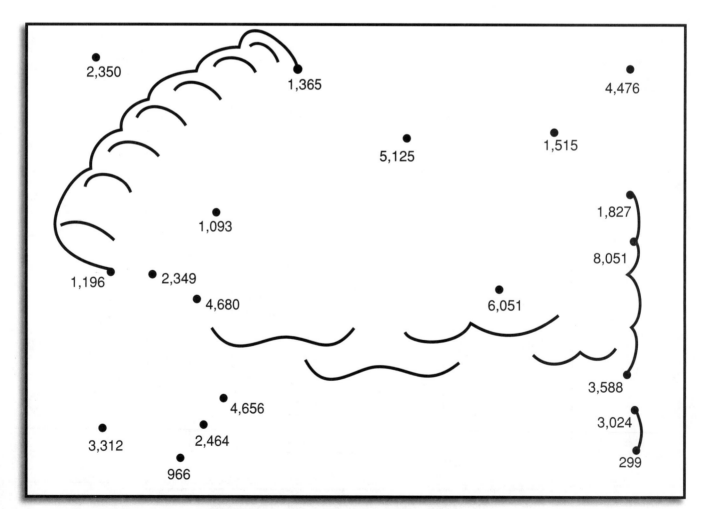

2,350
1,365
4,476
5,125
1,515
1,827
8,051
1,093
1,196   2,349
4,680   6,051
3,588
4,656
3,024
3,312   2,464
299
966

In a Galaxy Far Away

Multiply. To find the path to the center, look for three products whose sum is 20,560.

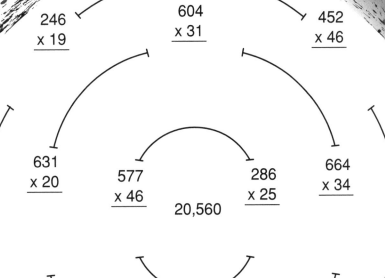

246
x 19

604
x 31

452
x 46

631
x 20

577
x 46

286
x 25

664
x 34

20,560

214
x 57

168
x 52

283
x 47

Zoom, Zoom!

Multiply. Circle the products in the puzzle.

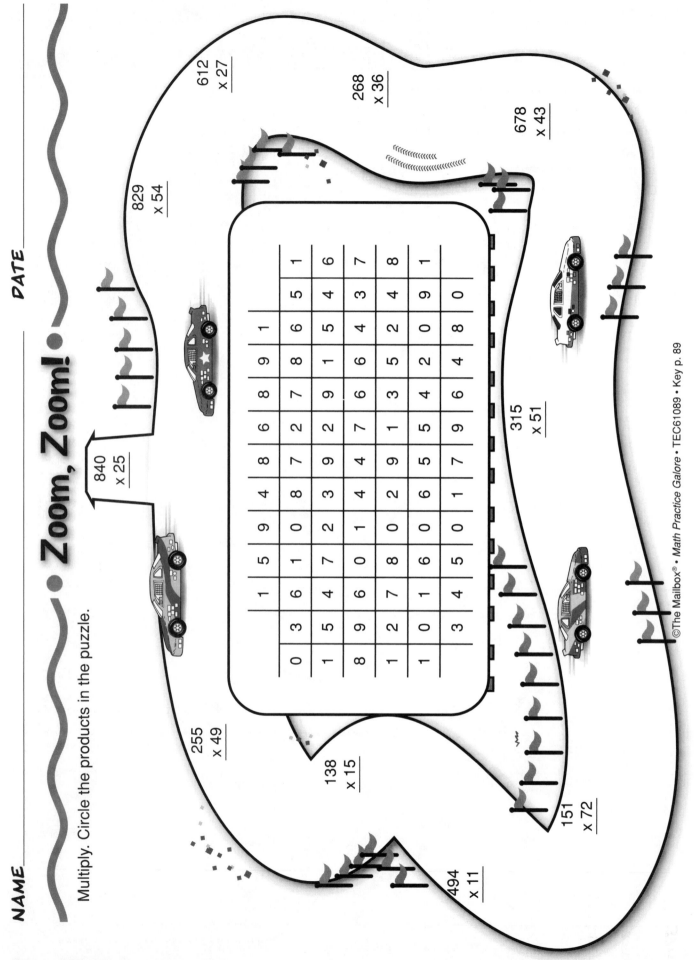

0	3	1	5	9	4	8	6	9	1	5	1
1	5	6	1	0	8	7	2	8	6	4	6
8	9	4	7	2	3	9	7	1	5	3	7
1	2	6	0	1	4	4	6	6	4	4	8
1	0	7	8	0	2	9	1	3	2	2	8
1	1	1	6	0	6	5	3	5	0	9	1
3	4	5	5	0	1	7	9	6	8	0	

840
x 25

829
x 54

612
x 27

268
x 36

678
x 43

255
x 49

138
x 15

315
x 51

151
x 72

494
x 11

• Just Chillin' •

Multiply. Write the products in the puzzle.

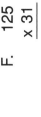

Across

A. 411
    x 70

C. 188
    x 27

E. 301
    x 33

G. 592
    x 46

Down

A. 591
    x 45

B. 905
    x 85

C. 236
    x 22

D. 731
    x 17

D. 304
    x 58

F. 125
    x 31

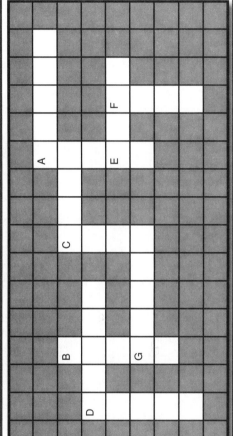

• Get Hooked •

Multiply. Cut out the answer boxes. Glue each box to its matching space.

311 x 232	713 x 309	630 x 505	910 x 644	6,004 x 356
542 x 550	2,043 x 150	456 x 122	670 x 507	4,951 x 238

©The Mailbox® • *Math Practice Galore* • TEC61089 • Key p. 89

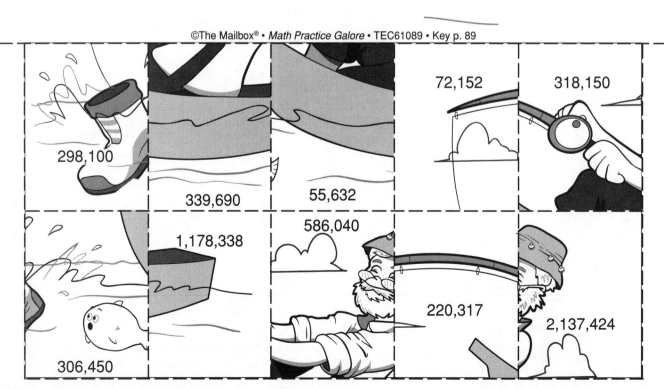

72,152

318,150

298,100

339,690

55,632

1,178,338

586,040

220,317

2,137,424

306,450

• Juggle the Numbers! •

Write each number from the number bank in a square. If you are correct, the product in each row and column is the number in the circle.

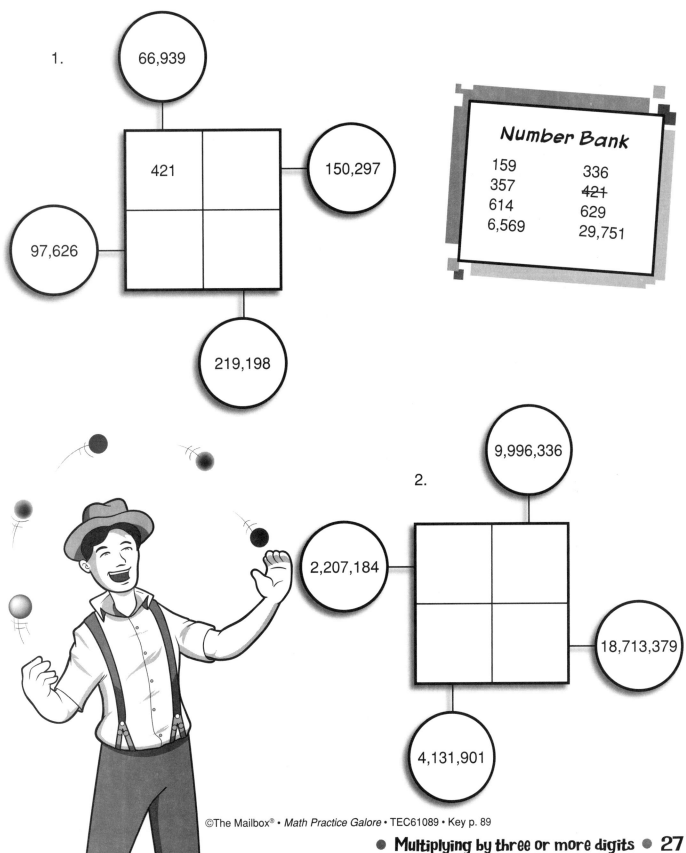

1.

66,939

421   150,297

97,626

219,198

Number Bank

159   336
357   ~~421~~
614   629
6,569   29,751

2.

9,996,336

2,207,184

18,713,379

4,131,901

• Plant Problem •

Round to the greatest place value and estimate. Cut out the puzzle strips with the matching answers. Then glue each strip in the corresponding column. One strip will not be used.

A. 168 x 42 ≈ _____

B. 780 x 33 ≈ _____

C. 46 x 96 ≈ _____

D. 465 x 21 ≈ _____

E. 508 x 78 ≈ _____

F. 268 x 44 ≈ _____

G. 608 x 31 ≈ _____

H. 103 x 57 ≈ _____

I. 327 x 25 ≈ _____

J. 498 x 32 ≈ _____

K. 39 x 97 ≈ _____

L. 89 x 83 ≈ _____

M. 95 x 74 ≈ _____

A	B	C	D	E	F	G	H	I	J	K	L	M

5,000	8,000	40,000	6,000	10,000	7,000	6,400	9,000	15,000	12,000	18,000	7,200	24,000	4,000
A	W	E	D	T		E		T	D	I	E	H	H
R	G	E	R	D		W		S	N	E	Y	A	A
	T	H	F	T	R	F	L	O	E		E	O	W
A	T		S	T		P		N	W	A	T	H	O
O	G	I	?	W	T	A		W	N	G	A	R	H
L	A	Z	D	A	!	Y	A	I	Y		Y		S

NAME_____ DATE _____

• Have Some Cake! •

Estimate each product to its greatest place value. If you are correct, the sum of the products on each slice will be the same.

B. 73 x 97 ≈

C. 54 x 38 ≈

J.
49 x 23 ≈

K.
112 x 58 ≈

A. 36 x 52 ≈

D. 674 x 12 ≈

I. 593 x 14 ≈

L. 53 x 18 ≈

P. 487 x 14 ≈

M. 78 x 49 ≈

O.
221 x 24 ≈

N.
514 x 12 ≈

H. 277 x 13 ≈

E. 84 x 54 ≈

G. 415 x 12 ≈

F. 335 x 13 ≈

Busy Town Bakery
Sum of the products on each slice = _____

• It's Magical! •

Divide. Then cross off the digits from each quotient in the corresponding row of the grid. If you are correct, the sum of the remaining digits in each row will be 10.

| 1. | $48 \div 3 =$ | _16_ | | 2. | $49 \div 7 =$ | _7_ |

| 1 | X | X | 8 | 1 | X |

| 3. | $96 \div 8 =$ ____ | | 4. | $65 \div 5 =$ ____ |

| 1 | 2 | 1 | 3 | 4 | 6 |

| 5. | $24 \div 4 =$ ____ | | 6. | $90 \div 9 =$ ____ |

| 5 | 1 | 0 | 6 | 2 | 3 |

| 7. | $78 \div 2 =$ ____ | | 8. | $91 \div 7 =$ ____ |

| 1 | 9 | 1 | 3 | 3 | 9 |

| 9. | $64 \div 8 =$ ____ | | 10. | $99 \div 3 =$ ____ |

| 8 | 1 | 4 | 3 | 3 | 5 |

| 11. | $81 \div 9 =$ ____ | | 12. | $42 \div 6 =$ ____ |

| 1 | 1 | 7 | 3 | 9 | 5 |

| 13. | $35 \div 5 =$ ____ | | 14. | $14 \div 7 =$ ____ |

| 7 | 1 | 2 | 2 | 3 | 4 |

| 15. | $92 \div 4 =$ ____ | | 16. | $68 \div 2 =$ ____ |

| 3 | 7 | 2 | 3 | 3 | 4 |

| 17. | $48 \div 6 =$ ____ | | 18. | $57 \div 3 =$ ____ |

| 2 | 8 | 4 | 4 | 1 | 9 |

| 19. | $54 \div 9 =$ ____ | | 20. | $72 \div 8 =$ ____ |

| 1 | 9 | 7 | 1 | 1 | 6 |

• Underwater Diner •

Answer: Peanut butter and jellyfish

To find the riddle that matches the answer, divide. Lightly shade the circle beside your answer. Then write the shaded letters in the puzzle.

1. 3⟌66   (WHA) 22
           (WOU) 32

2. 6⟌36   (LDA) 8
           (TTY) 6

3. 2⟌94   (SHA) 42
           (PEO) 47

4. 7⟌98   (FSA) 14
           (RKE) 16

5. 5⟌75   (ATF) 13
           (NDW) 15

6. 8⟌32   (REN) 6
           (ICH) 4

7. 4⟌68   (CHF) 16
           (WOU) 17

8. 9⟌45   (LDA) 5
           (RIE) 6

9. 7⟌84   (SAN) 17
           (SHA) 12

10. 2⟌88   (DABI) 42
           (RKOR) 44

11. 3⟌72   (GHA) 34
           (DER) 24

12. 5⟌40   (IFIT) 8
           (MBUR) 6

13. 6⟌66   (GERF) 13
           (WENT) 11

14. 8⟌80   (ORASN) 11
           (TOADI) 10

15. 4⟌52   (NER?) 13
           (ACK?) 14

Question:

1		2			3		4		5		6			
7		8				9	10			11				
12				13			14				15			

©The Mailbox® • *Math Practice Galore* • TEC61089 • Key p. 90

• On a Mission •

Divide. Write the quotient in the puzzle. The first one has been done for you.

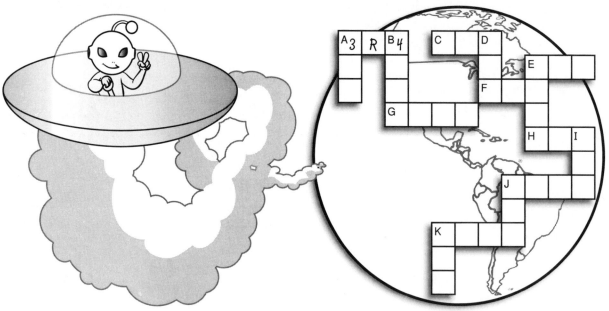

Across

A. $\begin{array}{r} 3\text{ R}4 \\ 7\overline{)25} \\ -21 \\ \hline 4 \end{array}$

C. $6\overline{)33}$

E. $4\overline{)19}$

F. $8\overline{)18}$

G. $5\overline{)96}$

H. $9\overline{)16}$

J. $4\overline{)85}$

K. $3\overline{)71}$

Down

A. $7\overline{)23}$

B. $2\overline{)91}$

D. $3\overline{)11}$

E. $2\overline{)85}$

I. $4\overline{)29}$

J. $6\overline{)14}$

K. $8\overline{)21}$

• One Funny Chicken •

Divide. To answer each riddle, find the quotient each time it appears in the chart. Then write the word(s) in the space(s).

8 R2	5 R8	28 R1	9 R3	22 R2
from	around	chicken	peck-nics	feed
5 R8	11 R5	5 R2	8 R2	11 R2
the	Fry-day	other	scratch	hen-velope
9 R2	5 R8	24 R3	5 R2	9 R2
rubber	cluck	comedi-hens	slide	chicken

1. 68 ÷ 3 = _____
Why can't a chicken ever get rich?
Because it works for chicken
_____!

2. 39 ÷ 4 = _____
What do chicken families do on Saturday?
They go on "_____"!

3. 71 ÷ 6 = _____
Which day of the week do chickens
hate the most?
"_____"!

4. 47 ÷ 5 = _____
Why did the chicken bounce across
the road?
It was a _____
_____!

5. 79 ÷ 7 = _____
How does a chicken mail a letter?
It uses a "_____"!

6. 53 ÷ 9 = _____
How long do chickens work?
_____ _____
"_____"!

7. 57 ÷ 2 = _____
Why did the rooster run away?
He was _____!

8. 17 ÷ 3 = _____
Why did the chicken cross the
playground?
To get to the _____
_____!

9. 99 ÷ 4 = _____
Who tells the best chicken jokes?
"_____"!

10. 66 ÷ 8 = _____
How do chickens bake a cake?
_____ _____!

• Braving the Rapids •

Divide. Write the answer in the boxes beside each problem, using one number or letter from each column below. One number in each column will not be used.

1. $3\overline{)460}$
2. $5\overline{)396}$
3. $8\overline{)253}$
4. $7\overline{)681}$
5. $4\overline{)566}$

6. $9\overline{)413}$
7. $5\overline{)774}$
8. $2\overline{)129}$
9. $6\overline{)350}$
10. $7\overline{)827}$

2	8	7	3	1
1	5	R	R	3
4	5	5	R	4
1	3	4	8	
5	4	R	R	
6	1	8	2	

9	1	1	2	2
1	2	5	R	2
1	5	9	R	1
3	9	7	1	3
7	7	4	R	4
6	4	3	1	5

• Who Stole It? •

Use the code to divide. Cross off the quotients inside the handcuffs. The sum of the remainders of the unused quotients will reveal the thief.

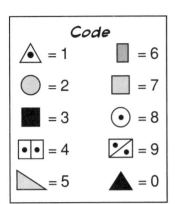

A. ⚃) ◯ ▢ ▲

B. ▯) ◺ △ ⬔

C. ⬔) ▢ ▲ ◺

D. ◺) ■ ⚃ ■

E. ◯) ⚃ ◯ ◺

F. ▢) ⊙ ▢ ▲

G. ■) ◯ ⬔ ⬔

H. ▯) ⊙ ⚃ ▢

Suspects
1 = Wacky Wayne
2 = Foolish Fred
3 = Dangerous Dan
4 = Chancy Charlie
5 = Wild Willie
6 = Daredevil Dave
7 = Fearless Fran
8 = Bad Bob
9 = Naughty Ned
10 = Rowdy Rick

The thief is

_____.

NAME_____   DATE_____

• Refreshing •

Which hand should you use to stir lemonade?

Divide. Cut out the answer boxes. Glue each box to its matching space in the grid to reveal the answer to the riddle.

A. 3)924	B. 5)538	C. 4)819
D. 8)642	E. 2)815	F. 7)494
G. 4)835	H. 6)643	I. 3)617
J. 9)949	K. 5)252	L. 6)544

©The Mailbox® • *Math Practice Galore* • TEC61089 • Key p. 90

208 R3	407 R1	308	107 R1	204 R3	70 R4
☆	SHO	NE USE ⬩HER ⬩ULD	☆		
107 R3	205 R2	50 R2	80 R2	105 R4	90 R4
ITH			YOU		

• Wandering Through the Grapevines •

Divide. Circle the problems that have a zero in the quotient. Connect the circles to show the path through the maze.

Start

$2\overline{)215}$

$5\overline{)704}$ $7\overline{)639}$

$6\overline{)340}$ $2\overline{)294}$ $7\overline{)216}$ $9\overline{)972}$

$9\overline{)218}$

$8\overline{)867}$ $6\overline{)425}$

$7\overline{)784}$ $4\overline{)429}$

$9\overline{)996}$ $5\overline{)568}$

$3\overline{)590}$

$6\overline{)685}$ $8\overline{)839}$ $2\overline{)418}$

Finish

NAME_____   DATE_____

• To the Rescue •

Divide.
Write the quotient and remainder on the lines.

	Quotient		Remainder
A. 21)357	___	17	___
B. 18)964	___	63	___
C. 31)518	___	38	___
D. 47)519	___	13	___
E. 39)990	___	40	___
F. 15)315	___	21	___
G. 50)961	___	30	___
H. 41)639	___	39	___
I. 17)438	___	38	___
J. 28)814	___	31	___

The number in each middle section should be the sum of the quotient and remainder.

● Robotic Parts ●

Follow the rules to write the correct numbers from the number bank on each robot's belly, hand, or foot.

Rules
1. When you divide the left hand by the belly, you get the right foot.
2. When you divide the right hand by the belly, you get the left foot.

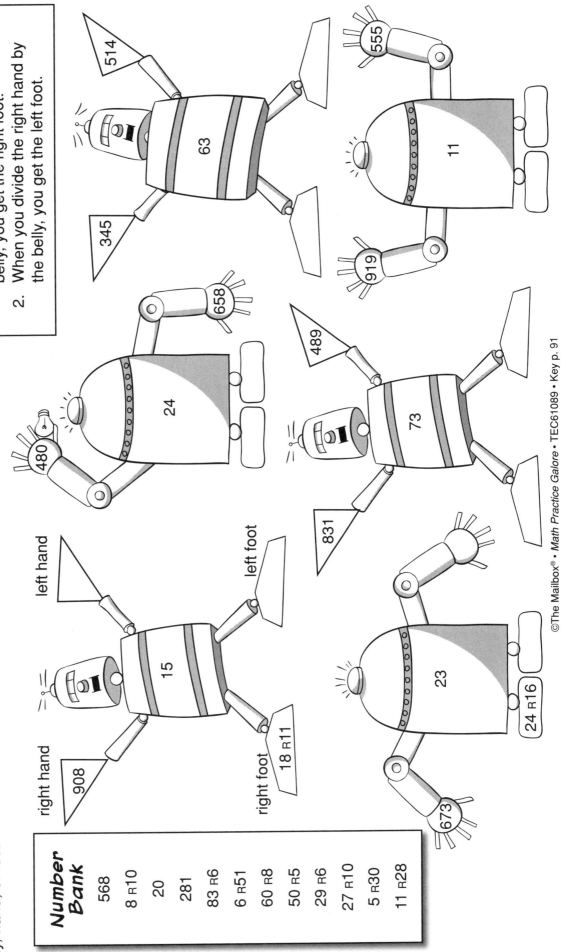

right hand

left hand

right foot

left foot

Number Bank

568
8 R10
20
281
83 R6
6 R51
60 R8
50 R5
29 R6
27 R10
5 R30
11 R28

• Step Right Up! •

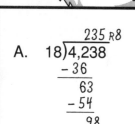

Divide. Write the answers on the stones. The last digit of one quotient is the first digit of the next.

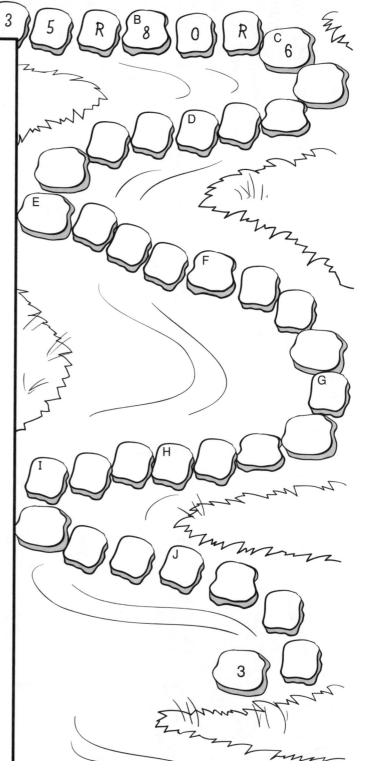

A.
$$\begin{array}{r} 235\,\text{R}8 \\ 18\overline{)4{,}238} \\ -36 \\ \hline 63 \\ -54 \\ \hline 98 \\ -90 \\ \hline 8 \end{array}$$

B.
$$\begin{array}{r} 80\,\text{R}6 \\ 25\overline{)2{,}006} \\ -200 \\ \hline 6 \\ -6 \\ \hline 6 \end{array}$$

C. $11\overline{)7{,}429}$

D. $52\overline{)2{,}259}$

E. $40\overline{)1{,}256}$

F. $66\overline{)4{,}150}$

G. $10\overline{)8{,}192}$

H. $85\overline{)1{,}787}$

I. $74\overline{)1{,}957}$

J. $39\overline{)1{,}388}$

• Don't Hold Your Breath •

Answer: Your breath

To find the riddle that matches the answer, divide. Lightly shade the circle beside your answer. Then write the shaded letters in the puzzle.

1. 38)5,920   (WHA) 155 R30
                (WHO) 155 R24

2. 14)3,101   (JUM) 220 R8
                (TIS) 221 R7

3. 79)9,013   (PED) 109 R27
                (LIG) 114 R7

4. 51)4,238   (INT) 82 R3
                (HTB) 83 R5

5. 62)2,874   (UTCA) 46 R22
                (OTHE) 48 R22

6. 23)2,962   (SWIM) 130 R1
                (NNOT) 128 R18

7. 90)6,687   (BEHE) 74 R27
                (MING) 81 R18

8. 45)1,445   (POOL) 33 R6
                (LDFO) 32 R5

9. 88)8,356   (RLO) 94 R84
                (TOD) 93 R17

10. 56)7,599   (NG?) 135 R39
                (AY?) 129 R13

Question:

1			2				3			4		
	5					6				7		
		8					9			10		

· Dare to Square ·

Divide. Write each remainder in the matching box. When you're finished, the sum of each row, column, and diagonal of the square should equal 15.

A. $12\overline{)2{,}439}$

B. $83\overline{)3{,}327}$

C. $27\overline{)9{,}455}$

D. $12\overline{)7{,}928}$

E. $11\overline{)2{,}272}$

F. $53\overline{)5{,}779}$

G. $18\overline{)7{,}219}$

H. $92\overline{)7{,}364}$

I. $58\overline{)4{,}069}$

D.	A.	H.
G.	C.	I.
E.	B.	F.

• Take the Wheel! •

Divide. Write each remainder in the matching circle. When you're finished, the sum of the three numbers in each straight line should equal 21.

A. $37\overline{)3,748}$

B. $54\overline{)3,245}$

C. $35\overline{)7,251}$

D. $38\overline{)1,912}$

E. $32\overline{)8,964}$

F. $28\overline{)1,130}$

G. $12\overline{)4,892}$

H. $18\overline{)7,209}$

I. $23\overline{)1,157}$

• Division with zero in the quotient • 43

• At the Ballpark •

Round each number to the greatest place value and estimate. Check your answers using the sign.

Catcher + Pitcher + First Base = 130
Catcher + Pitcher + Second Base + Right Field = 130
Catcher + Pitcher + Shortstop + Center Field = 130
Catcher + Pitcher + Third Base + Left Field = 130

$2{,}428 \div 49 \approx$

_____

CENTER FIELD

$5{,}952 \div 98 \approx$

_____

LEFT FIELD

$7{,}306 \div 95 \approx$

_____

SECOND BASE

$1{,}270 \div 53 \approx$

_____

RIGHT FIELD

$2{,}286 \div 41 \approx$

_____

SHORTSTOP

$872 \div 31 \approx$

_____

THIRD BASE

$591 \div 19 \approx$

_____

PITCHER

$861 \div 14 \approx$

_____

FIRST BASE

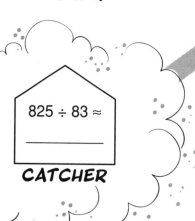

$825 \div 83 \approx$

_____

CATCHER

©The Mailbox® • *Math Practice Galore* • TEC61089 • Key p. 91

44 • **Estimating quotients** •

• Art by You •

Round each number to the greatest place value and then estimate.
Cut out the answer boxes. Glue each box to its matching space in the
grid to reveal the picture.

A. 3,099 ÷ 97 ≈ _____

B. 1,340 ÷ 51 ≈ _____

C. 3,809 ÷ 75 ≈ _____

D. 1,014 ÷ 96 ≈ _____

E. 4,280 ÷ 98 ≈ _____

F. 3,172 ÷ 49 ≈ _____

G. 7,498 ÷ 95 ≈ _____

H. 4,445 ÷ 53 ≈ _____

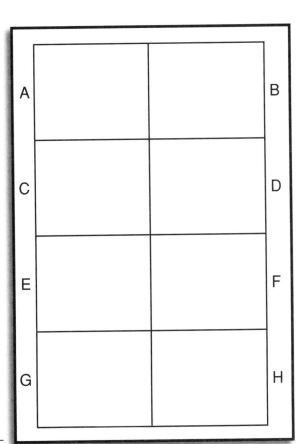

©The Mailbox® • *Math Practice Galore* • TEC61089 • Key p. 91

30		50	20		80
	70	10		60	40

• Bull's-eye! •

Circle each fraction that is less than $\frac{1}{2}$. Cross out each fraction that is greater than $\frac{1}{2}$. Shade each fraction that is equivalent to $\frac{1}{2}$ to show the bull's path to the bull's-eye.

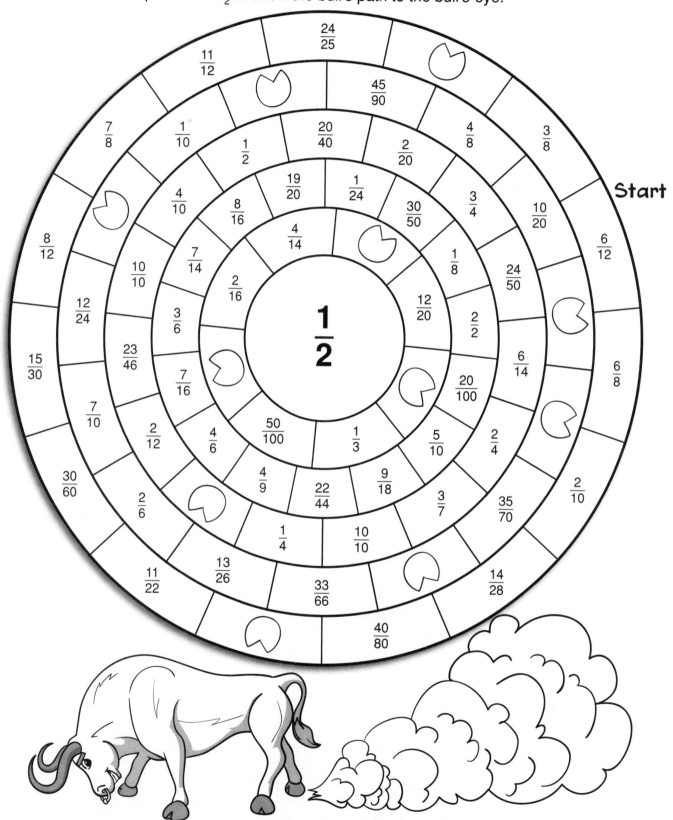

The Getaway

Find the least common multiple for each set of numbers.
Write your answer in word form in the puzzle.

Across

A.
| 6 |
| 12 |

B.
| 7 |
| 9 |

C.
| 30 |
| 6 |

F.
| 5 |
| 12 |

I.
| 7 |
| 8 |

J.
| 12 |
| 10 |

K.
| 11 |
| 3 |

Down

A.
| 5 |
| 20 |

D.
| 25 |
| 15 |

E.
| 8 |
| 20 |

G.
| 12 |
| 9 |

H.
| 6 |
| 9 |

©The Mailbox® • Math Practice Galore • TEC61089 • Key p. 92

• Cut! •

Find the greatest common factor. Then write your answer in the puzzle.

| A | 90 | 100 | | B | 24 | 12 | | C | 16 | 8 | | D | 45 | 60 | | E | 18 | 27 |

| F | 12 | 6 | | G | 150 | 80 | | H | 72 | 45 | | I | 121 | 33 |

| J | 15 | 25 | | K | 70 | 42 | | L | 143 | 55 |

If you have solved each problem correctly, each pair of numbers will have a sum of 20 and each group of three will have a sum of 30.

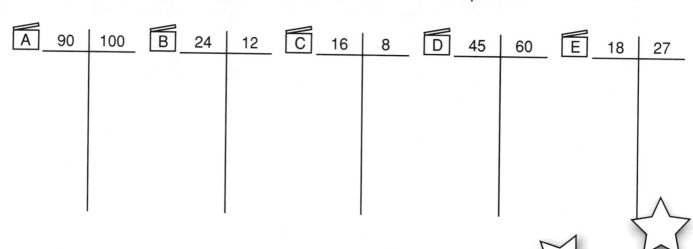

• Piece by Piece •

Write each fraction in simplest form. Then use the answer to complete the puzzle below.

A. $\dfrac{36}{48}$ =

B. $\dfrac{22}{88}$ =

C. $\dfrac{28}{42}$ =

D. $\dfrac{18}{27}$ =

E. $\dfrac{50}{75}$ =

F. $\dfrac{45}{90}$ =

G. $\dfrac{27}{54}$ =

H. $\dfrac{21}{42}$ =

I. $\dfrac{25}{100}$ =

J. $\dfrac{9}{36}$ =

K. $\dfrac{30}{40}$ =

L. $\dfrac{21}{28}$ =

$\dfrac{1}{4}$	A	F	$\dfrac{2}{3}$
E	H	L	B
K	C	J	G
$\dfrac{1}{2}$	I	D	$\dfrac{3}{4}$

Rules:
1. Each fraction must appear only once in each row.
2. Each fraction must appear only once in each column.
3. Each fraction must appear only once in each boldfaced box.

©The Mailbox® • *Math Practice Galore* • TEC61089 • Key p. 92

• **Simplest form** • **49**

•It's Hot in Here!•

What do volcanoes like to read?

Draw an X over each incorrect number sentence and an O around each correct number sentence. The winner will have three marks in a row. Write the letter of each gameboard on its matching line below the volcano.

A.

$\frac{1}{2} = \frac{2}{3}$	$\frac{2}{5} = \frac{1}{3}$	$\frac{5}{10} = \frac{4}{8}$
$\frac{3}{6} = \frac{2}{4}$	$\frac{6}{12} = \frac{2}{4}$	$\frac{1}{5} = \frac{2}{6}$
$\frac{15}{30} = \frac{2}{4}$	$\frac{4}{5} = \frac{3}{8}$	$\frac{7}{8} = \frac{1}{2}$

Winner = _____

"_____ _____ _____ _____ _____ -ZINES"

neither wins   O wins   X wins   neither wins   O wins

G.

$\frac{1}{5} = \frac{6}{9}$	$\frac{1}{6} = \frac{2}{3}$	$\frac{5}{7} = \frac{4}{8}$
$\frac{1}{5} = \frac{2}{10}$	$\frac{2}{5} = \frac{4}{10}$	$\frac{1}{2} = \frac{2}{3}$
$\frac{1}{3} = \frac{6}{9}$	$\frac{3}{4} = \frac{1}{2}$	$\frac{6}{12} = \frac{4}{8}$

Winner = _____

M.

$\frac{4}{5} = \frac{8}{10}$	$\frac{2}{3} = \frac{1}{6}$	$\frac{1}{4} = \frac{2}{5}$
$\frac{1}{3} = \frac{1}{4}$	$\frac{6}{9} = \frac{1}{3}$	$\frac{2}{8} = \frac{4}{16}$
$\frac{1}{2} = \frac{10}{20}$	$\frac{3}{5} = \frac{6}{10}$	$\frac{2}{5} = \frac{1}{12}$

Winner = _____

• Howdy •

Answer: A jolly rancher

To find the riddle that matches the answer, change each improper fraction to a mixed number or a whole number. Lightly color the circled letters of each answer. Write the letters in the puzzle.

1. $\frac{6}{5}$ =

   (TUR) $1\frac{5}{6}$

   (WHA) $1\frac{1}{5}$

2. $\frac{8}{3}$ =

   (TDO) $2\frac{2}{3}$

   (ART) $2\frac{3}{8}$

3. $\frac{3}{2}$ =

   (YOU) $1\frac{1}{2}$

   (STA) $1\frac{1}{3}$

4. $\frac{9}{7}$ =

   (TAM) $1\frac{9}{3}$

   (CAL) $1\frac{2}{7}$

5. $\frac{13}{6}$ =

   (AMR) $6\frac{1}{6}$

   (LAH) $2\frac{1}{6}$

6. $\frac{20}{5}$ =

   (AP) 4

   (TI) $3\frac{4}{5}$

7. $\frac{7}{4}$ =

   (BO) 3

   (PY) $1\frac{3}{4}$

8. $\frac{51}{5}$ =

   (CO) $10\frac{1}{5}$

   (UY) $5\frac{2}{5}$

9. $\frac{14}{3}$ =

   (WB) $4\frac{2}{3}$

   (CW) $3\frac{2}{3}$

10. $\frac{11}{2}$ =

   (ID) $4\frac{1}{2}$

   (OY) $5\frac{1}{2}$

Question:

1		2				3			
4		5				6		7	
	8	9		10		?			

NAME _____ DATE _____

• The Race Is On! •

Solve. Write each answer in simplest form. Then cut out each answer box and glue it to the matching spot on the grid.

A. $\frac{2}{6} + \frac{3}{6} =$	B. $\frac{7}{8} - \frac{3}{8} =$	C. $\frac{2}{12} + \frac{6}{12} =$	D. $\frac{15}{20} - \frac{7}{20} =$
E. $\frac{12}{15} - \frac{3}{15} =$	F. $\frac{6}{8} + \frac{4}{8} =$	G. $\frac{2}{7} + \frac{3}{7} =$	H. $1 - \frac{1}{5} =$
I. $\frac{1}{8} + \frac{2}{8} =$	J. $\frac{5}{9} + \frac{2}{9} =$	K. $\frac{6}{9} - \frac{4}{9} =$	L. $\frac{1}{3} + \frac{2}{3} =$

©The Mailbox® • *Math Practice Galore* • TEC61089 • Key p. 92

52 • Adding and subtracting like fractions •

•Shake-Up!•

Add. Write each answer in simplest form. Cut out the puzzle strip with the matching answer. Then glue the strip to the grid.

A. $\dfrac{3}{4}$
   $+\dfrac{1}{8}$

B. $\dfrac{2}{5}$
   $+\dfrac{1}{2}$

C. $\dfrac{1}{4}$
   $+\dfrac{1}{3}$

D. $\dfrac{1}{6}$
   $+\dfrac{3}{4}$

E. $\dfrac{1}{2}$
   $+\dfrac{1}{4}$

F. $\dfrac{1}{3}$
   $+\dfrac{2}{4}$

G. $\dfrac{1}{8}$
   $+\dfrac{1}{2}$

H. $\dfrac{4}{9}$
   $+\dfrac{1}{18}$

A		B	C	D		E	F	G	H	

$\frac{11}{12}$ R	E	$\frac{7}{8}$	W	$\frac{3}{4}$ H	$\frac{9}{10}$ H	$\frac{5}{8}$ O	$\frac{5}{6}$ D	$\frac{7}{12}$ E	$\frac{1}{2}$	
	S	M	I	H	L	K	A	K	E	S
	F	C	O	R	M	M	O	E	?	
R	V			O	N	S	U	E		
O	W			S			!	C		

• A Great Mystery •

Add. Write each answer in simplest form. Then circle each answer in the code box below. Draw the circled codes to complete the grid.

A. $\dfrac{1}{10}$
$+ \dfrac{3}{5}$

B. $\dfrac{2}{7}$
$+ \dfrac{3}{5}$

C. $\dfrac{1}{8}$
$+ \dfrac{2}{3}$

D. $\dfrac{5}{24}$
$+ \dfrac{3}{4}$

E. $\dfrac{2}{5}$
$+ \dfrac{1}{6}$

F. $\dfrac{1}{9}$
$+ \dfrac{1}{4}$

G. $\dfrac{1}{3}$
$+ \dfrac{2}{4}$

H. $\dfrac{8}{18}$
$+ \dfrac{2}{6}$

I. $\dfrac{1}{12}$
$+ \dfrac{2}{6}$

J. $\dfrac{1}{5}$
$+ \dfrac{1}{2}$

The Suspects

Wild Bill

Wild Pete

Wild Jane

Code

A. $\dfrac{7}{10}$ = [   ] , $\dfrac{5}{8}$ = [   ]

B. $\dfrac{3}{7}$ = [   ] , $\dfrac{31}{35}$ = [   ]

C. $\dfrac{1}{6}$ = [   ] , $\dfrac{19}{24}$ = [   ]

D. $\dfrac{23}{24}$ = [   ] , $\dfrac{2}{5}$ = [   ]

E. $\dfrac{1}{4}$ = [   ] , $\dfrac{17}{30}$ = [   ]

F. $\dfrac{13}{36}$ = [   ] , $\dfrac{1}{4}$ = [   ]

G. $\dfrac{5}{6}$ = [   ] , $\dfrac{1}{4}$ = [   ]

H. $\dfrac{5}{18}$ = [   ] , $\dfrac{7}{9}$ = [   ]

I. $\dfrac{5}{12}$ = [   ] , $\dfrac{1}{4}$ = [   ]

J. $\dfrac{7}{10}$ = [   ] , $\dfrac{2}{8}$ = [   ]

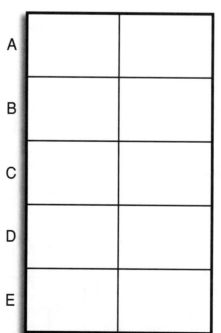

Your correct answers will reveal the guilty person's fingerprint.

• Rat Race •

Add. Follow the path of each correct answer.

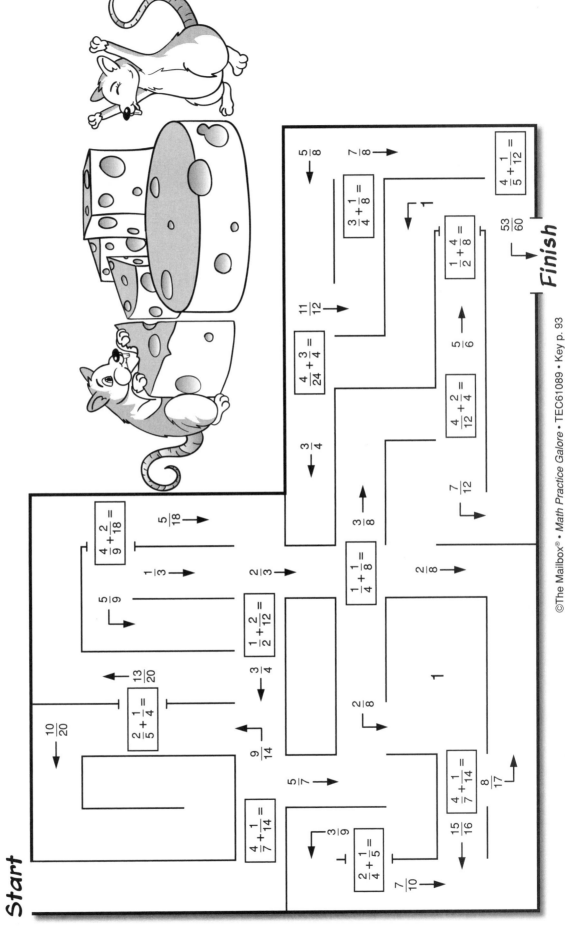

Start

Finish

$\frac{4}{9} + \frac{2}{18} =$ $\frac{5}{18} \rightarrow$

$\frac{5}{9}$ $\frac{1}{3} \rightarrow$ $\frac{2}{3} \rightarrow$

$\frac{1}{2} + \frac{2}{12} =$

$\frac{3}{4}$

$\frac{2}{5} + \frac{1}{4} =$ $\frac{13}{20} \rightarrow$

$\frac{10}{20}$

$\frac{9}{14}$

$\frac{2}{8}$

$\frac{1}{4} + \frac{1}{8} =$ $\frac{2}{8} \rightarrow$

$\frac{2}{8}$

1

$\frac{4}{7} + \frac{1}{14} =$

$\frac{5}{7} \rightarrow$

$\frac{2}{4} + \frac{1}{5} =$ $\frac{3}{9}$ $\frac{7}{10} \rightarrow$

$\frac{4}{7} + \frac{1}{14} =$ $\frac{15}{16}$ $\frac{8}{17} \rightarrow$

$\frac{3}{8}$

$\frac{7}{12}$

$\frac{4}{24} + \frac{3}{4} =$ $\frac{11}{12} \rightarrow$

$\frac{3}{4}$

$\frac{4}{12} + \frac{2}{4} =$

$\frac{5}{6} \rightarrow$

$\frac{3}{4} + \frac{1}{8} =$ $\frac{5}{8}$

1

$\frac{1}{2} + \frac{4}{8} =$

$\frac{7}{8} \rightarrow$

$\frac{4}{5} + \frac{1}{12} =$ $\frac{53}{60}$

• On the Right Path •

In each path, subtract to solve the first problem. Then subtract the next fraction from the first problem's difference. Continue until you reach the end of the path. Color the path that has the correct final answer in its simplest form.

$$2\frac{8}{15}$$
$$-\ \frac{1}{6}$$

$$2\frac{23}{24}$$
$$-\ \frac{1}{2}$$

$$\square$$
$$-\ \frac{1}{2}$$

$$1\frac{37}{40}$$
$$-\ \frac{3}{4}$$

$$\square$$
$$-\ \frac{3}{4}$$

$$\square$$
$$-\ \frac{2}{3}$$

$$\square$$
$$-\ \frac{3}{10}$$

$$\square$$
$$-\ \frac{3}{8}$$

$$\square$$
$$-\ \frac{2}{4}$$

$$\square$$
$$-\ \frac{1}{6}$$

$$\square$$
$$-\ \frac{1}{2}$$

$$\square$$
$$-\ \frac{2}{4}$$

$$\square$$
$$-\ \frac{1}{5}$$

$$\square$$
$$-\ \frac{1}{2}$$

$$\square$$
$$-\ \frac{2}{4}$$

Final Answer

$$\frac{1}{4}$$

Final Answer

$$\frac{2}{3}$$

Final Answer

$$\frac{1}{2}$$

• Fishin' for Fractions •

Subtract. Write your answer in simplest form. Circle the word form of your answer in the puzzle.

A. $\dfrac{9}{10}$ $-\dfrac{1}{2}$

B. $\dfrac{7}{8}$ $-\dfrac{2}{16}$

C. $\dfrac{3}{4}$ $-\dfrac{7}{12}$

D. $\dfrac{5}{6}$ $-\dfrac{11}{24}$

E. $\dfrac{11}{22}$ $-\dfrac{4}{8}$

F. $\dfrac{4}{14}$ $-\dfrac{1}{7}$

G. $\dfrac{8}{10}$ $-\dfrac{1}{5}$

H. $\dfrac{10}{10}$ $-\dfrac{1}{5}$

I. $\dfrac{4}{9}$ $-\dfrac{1}{3}$

J. $\dfrac{5}{6}$ $-\dfrac{1}{3}$

K. $\dfrac{2}{5}$ $-\dfrac{2}{10}$

L. $\dfrac{11}{24}$ $-\dfrac{1}{3}$

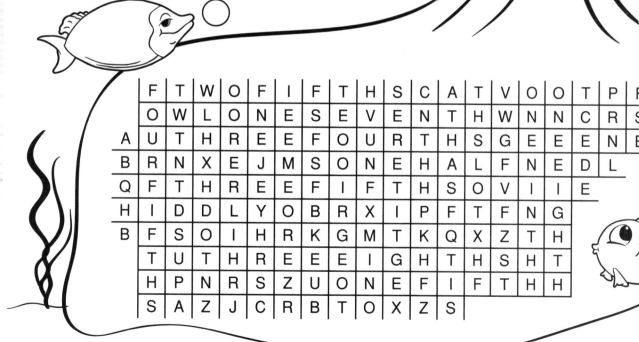

	F	T	W	O	F	I	F	T	H	S	C	A	T	V	O	O	T	P	F
	O	W	L	O	N	E	S	E	V	E	N	T	H	W	N	N	C	R	S
A	U	T	H	R	E	E	F	O	U	R	T	H	S	G	E	E	E	N	E
B	R	N	X	E	J	M	S	O	N	E	H	A	L	F	N	E	D	L	
Q	F	T	H	R	E	E	F	I	F	T	H	S	O	V	I	I	E		
H	I	D	D	L	Y	O	B	R	X	I	P	F	T	F	N	G			
B	F	S	O	I	H	R	K	G	M	T	K	Q	X	Z	T	H			
	T	U	T	H	R	E	E	E	I	G	H	T	H	S	H	T			
	H	P	N	R	S	Z	U	O	N	E	F	I	F	T	H	H			
	S	A	Z	J	C	R	B	T	O	X	Z	S							

• Knocked Around •

Subtract. Color the box if the answer is correct to show the path the ball takes through the pinball machine. The sum of all colored numerators should equal the low score. The sum of all colored denominators should equal the high score.

START

Low Score
00091

High Score
00180

$\frac{7}{8}$ $-\frac{1}{6}$ $\overline{\frac{17}{24}}$	$\frac{3}{4}$ $-\frac{1}{3}$ $\overline{\frac{5}{12}}$	$\frac{11}{12}$ $-\frac{1}{5}$ $\overline{\frac{42}{60}}$
	$\frac{6}{10}$ $-\frac{1}{5}$ $\overline{\frac{2}{5}}$	$\frac{8}{9}$ $-\frac{1}{4}$ $\overline{\frac{23}{36}}$

$\frac{4}{5}$ $-\frac{1}{3}$ $\overline{\frac{7}{15}}$	$\frac{9}{11}$ $-\frac{2}{3}$ $\overline{\frac{5}{33}}$	$\frac{7}{9}$ $-\frac{1}{3}$ $\overline{\frac{1}{3}}$	$\frac{3}{4}$ $-\frac{1}{5}$ $\overline{\frac{11}{20}}$
$\frac{9}{10}$ $-\frac{1}{4}$ $\overline{\frac{13}{20}}$	$\frac{9}{12}$ $-\frac{1}{2}$ $\overline{\frac{1}{3}}$	$\frac{5}{6}$ $-\frac{1}{2}$ $\overline{\frac{1}{3}}$	$\frac{5}{7}$ $-\frac{1}{14}$ $\overline{\frac{4}{7}}$
$\frac{6}{7}$ $-\frac{3}{8}$ $\overline{\frac{25}{56}}$	$\frac{3}{4}$ $-\frac{1}{6}$ $\overline{\frac{7}{12}}$	$\frac{6}{8}$ $-\frac{1}{3}$ $\overline{\frac{11}{24}}$	$\frac{5}{9}$ $-\frac{1}{3}$ $\overline{\frac{3}{9}}$

FINISH

Tell Me More!

How many pounds of marshmallows are sold in the United States each year?

Add. Write each answer in simplest form. Use a ruler to connect the dots for each pair of matching sums. Write the letters that do not have a line through them in order from left to right on the lines below.

More than

— — — — — — — — —

pounds!

$1\frac{1}{3}$ $+\,2\frac{1}{3}$ •	$2\frac{1}{4}$ $+\,4\frac{2}{4}$ •	$3\frac{1}{5}$ $+\,1\frac{3}{5}$ •	$15\frac{3}{10}$ $+\,5\frac{3}{10}$ •	$1\frac{9}{15}$ $+\,3\frac{4}{15}$ •	$6\frac{1}{9}$ $+\,1\frac{6}{9}$ •

$2\frac{9}{21}$ $+\,2\frac{9}{21}$ •

• $2\frac{13}{30}$ $+\,2\frac{13}{30}$

N   I   C   N   E   T
N   U   C   O
A   I
Y   M   C
Z   K   T   L
I   O   N   B   B   L
R   G   S   A

$11\frac{13}{30}$ $+\,9\frac{5}{30}$ •

• $10\frac{3}{6}$ $+\,1\frac{2}{6}$

• $6\frac{9}{18}$ $+\,5\frac{6}{18}$	• $5\frac{2}{8}$ $+\,1\frac{4}{8}$	• $4\frac{1}{9}$ $+\,3\frac{6}{9}$	• $2\frac{1}{6}$ $+\,1\frac{3}{6}$	• $1\frac{1}{7}$ $+\,3\frac{5}{7}$	• $4\frac{1}{10}$ $+\,\frac{7}{10}$

• All Abuzz •

Subtract. Find the answer in the grid. The answer may be shown more than once. To solve the riddle, write each word in order.

1. $4\frac{1}{2} - \frac{1}{2} =$ _____

What did the mother bee say to her son?

"_____" _____!

2. $5\frac{7}{8} - \frac{4}{8} =$ _____

What goes zzub, zzub?

A _____ _____

_____!

3. $1\frac{6}{7} - \frac{3}{7} =$ _____

Which queen can never wear a crown?

A _____ _____

4. $3\frac{5}{9} - 2\frac{4}{9} =$ _____

What do you call a bee with a low buzz?

A _____ _____

5. $11\frac{6}{11} - 9\frac{4}{11} =$ _____

What do you call a bee born in May?

A _____

6. $13\frac{3}{4} - 10\frac{2}{4} =$ _____

What kind of bee drops things?

A _____ _____

7. $2\frac{10}{11} - 1\frac{8}{11} =$ _____

Why do bees hum?

Because _____ _____

_____ the _____!

8. $8\frac{3}{5} - 7\frac{2}{5} =$ _____

What is better than a talking dog?

A _____ _____!

9. $9\frac{7}{12} - 3\frac{6}{12} =$ _____

Why do bees have sticky hair?

Because _____ _____

_____ _____!

10. $4\frac{5}{7} - 4\frac{3}{7} =$ _____

How do bees get to school?

On _____ "_____

_____"!

Grid:

$5\frac{3}{8}$ bee — $1\frac{3}{7}$ queen — $1\frac{2}{11}$ they — $2\frac{2}{11}$ maybe

$6\frac{1}{12}$ they — $\frac{2}{7}$ a — $3\frac{1}{4}$ fumble

$1\frac{2}{11}$ don't — 4 Bee-hive — $1\frac{1}{5}$ spelling — $5\frac{3}{8}$ flying — $1\frac{1}{9}$ mumble — $1\frac{1}{9}$ bee

$\frac{2}{7}$ school — $5\frac{3}{8}$ backward — $6\frac{1}{12}$ have — 4 yourself — $3\frac{1}{4}$ bee

$1\frac{2}{11}$ know — $1\frac{1}{5}$ bee — $\frac{2}{7}$ buzz

$1\frac{3}{7}$ bee — $6\frac{1}{12}$ honey — $1\frac{2}{11}$ words — $6\frac{1}{12}$ combs

• The Amazing Amazon •

Add. Write your answer in the puzzle. Then cross out each number used in the matching column. The first one has been done for you.

A. $14\frac{2}{9}$
   $+\ 3\frac{1}{3}$
   _____
   $17\frac{5}{9}$

B. $6\frac{4}{5}$
   $+\ 1\frac{1}{10}$

C. $19\frac{10}{11}$
   $+\ 3\frac{1}{22}$

D. $\frac{7}{10}$
   $+\ 4\frac{1}{5}$

E. $5\frac{4}{9}$
   $+\ 3\frac{1}{3}$

F. $13\frac{5}{10}$
   $+\ 5\frac{1}{4}$

G. $2\frac{2}{7}$
   $+\ 3\frac{1}{2}$

H. $12\frac{3}{5}$
   $+\ 6\frac{1}{4}$

I. $17\frac{2}{11}$
   $+\ 3\frac{1}{2}$

About how many species of insects can be found in the Amazon rain forest? Use the remaining numbers in the puzzle to write your answer beside the ★ in the chart.

				0	0	2	2
			0	2	2	2	4
		0	0	0	1	4	9
	0	1	1	1	5	7	9
	0	1	1	2	3	5	
	0	1	7	9	9		
0	0	2	7	8	8		
1	1	1	2	2	3	4	5	7	8

A. 1 7
B. 7
C. 9
D. 5
E. 9
F.
G.
H.
I.
★

• On Fire! •

Add. Write each letter on its matching numbered line. Then find the correct path through the maze below to answer the riddle question.

$$\underset{15\frac{7}{12}}{\rule{1.5cm}{0.4pt}}\ \underset{3\frac{13}{16}}{\rule{1cm}{0.4pt}}\ \underset{12\frac{7}{8}}{\rule{1cm}{0.4pt}}\quad \underset{1\frac{5}{6}}{\rule{1cm}{0.4pt}}\ \overset{O}{\underset{12\frac{1}{2}}{\rule{1cm}{0.4pt}}}\quad \overset{I}{\underset{7\frac{11}{12}}{\rule{1cm}{0.4pt}}}\ \underset{7\frac{5}{6}}{\rule{1cm}{0.4pt}}\ \underset{12\frac{1}{2}}{\rule{1cm}{0.4pt}}\ \overset{IG}{\underset{3\frac{13}{16}}{\rule{1cm}{0.4pt}}}\ \overset{T}{\underset{7\frac{5}{6}}{\rule{1cm}{0.4pt}}}\ \underset{7\frac{11}{12}}{\rule{1cm}{0.4pt}}\ \underset{13\frac{7}{12}}{\rule{1cm}{0.4pt}}$$

$$\underset{15\frac{7}{12}}{\rule{1cm}{0.4pt}}\ \underset{7\frac{5}{6}}{\rule{1cm}{0.4pt}}\ \overset{A}{\underset{7\frac{11}{12}}{\rule{1.5cm}{0.4pt}}}\quad \underset{7\frac{11}{12}}{\rule{1cm}{0.4pt}}\ \underset{7\frac{5}{6}}{\rule{1cm}{0.4pt}}\ \underset{1\frac{5}{6}}{\rule{1cm}{0.4pt}}\ \underset{13\frac{7}{12}}{\rule{1.5cm}{0.4pt}}\quad \overset{U}{\underset{13\frac{7}{12}}{\rule{1.5cm}{0.4pt}}}\ \underset{11\frac{13}{18}}{\rule{1cm}{0.4pt}}\ \underset{7\frac{5}{6}}{\rule{1cm}{0.4pt}}\ \underset{13\frac{4}{7}}{\rule{1cm}{0.4pt}}\ \underset{1\frac{5}{6}}{\rule{1cm}{0.4pt}}\ \underset{7\frac{5}{6}}{\rule{1cm}{0.4pt}}\ \underset{7\frac{11}{12}}{\rule{1cm}{0.4pt}}\ \underset{13\frac{7}{12}}{\rule{1cm}{0.4pt}}\ ?$$

D. $\frac{2}{3}$
$+\ 1\frac{1}{6}$

S. $3\frac{1}{3}$
$+\ 10\frac{1}{4}$

E. $2\frac{7}{12}$
$+\ 5\frac{1}{4}$

N. $7\frac{1}{14}$
$+\ 6\frac{1}{2}$

H. $\frac{5}{8}$
$+\ 3\frac{3}{16}$

W. $6\frac{1}{3}$
$+\ 9\frac{1}{4}$

F. $4\frac{1}{5}$
$+\ 8\frac{3}{10}$

R. $1\frac{5}{6}$
$+\ 6\frac{1}{12}$

P. $6\frac{1}{3}$
$+\ 5\frac{7}{18}$

Y. $5\frac{3}{8}$
$+\ 7\frac{1}{2}$

START

FINISH

• Round'em Up! •

Add. Write each answer in simplest form. Then unscramble the letters below to write each answer in word form.

A. $10\frac{2}{5}$
$+ 2\frac{5}{10}$

B. $2\frac{5}{12}$
$+ 9\frac{1}{8}$

C. $25\frac{2}{3}$
$+ 8\frac{2}{9}$

D. $15\frac{4}{9}$
$+ 4\frac{1}{2}$

E. $6\frac{5}{7}$
$+ 5\frac{1}{4}$

F. $14\frac{3}{10}$
$+ 1\frac{2}{6}$

G. $13\frac{3}{8}$
$+ 8\frac{2}{4}$

H. $9\frac{2}{5}$
$+ 1\frac{1}{3}$

A.   twelve and _____ - _____
                          enin   tsenth

B.   _____ and _____ twenty-fourths
             eleevn   hietrtne

C.   _____ and eight-_____
         tihtry-hrete   sintnh

D.   nineteen and _____ - _____
                             teesvnene   ihtegehents

E.   eleven and _____ - _____
                          wntety-eenvs   wntety-giehths

F.   _____ and nineteen-_____
            etffeni   hrititesht

G.   _____ and _____ -eighths
          ytntew-noe   evnse

H.   ten and _____ - _____
                       eleevn   tfieetfnsh

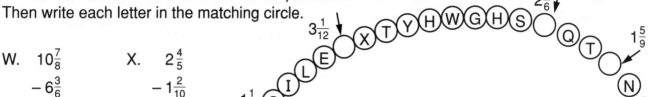

Mad Scientist

Subtract. Write each answer in the simplest form.
Then write each letter in the matching circle.

W. $10\frac{7}{8}$
$-\ 6\frac{3}{6}$

X. $2\frac{4}{5}$
$-\ 1\frac{2}{10}$

A. $1\frac{5}{6}$
$-\ \ \frac{1}{3}$

E. $9\frac{2}{3}$
$-\ 8\frac{1}{9}$

M. $15\frac{5}{7}$
$-\ 13\frac{1}{2}$

C. $8\frac{6}{9}$
$-\ 6\frac{1}{2}$

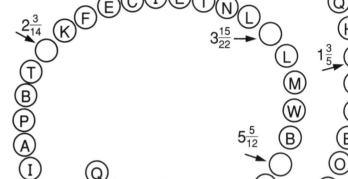

R. $13\frac{9}{10}$
$-\ 7\frac{1}{4}$

N. $5\frac{8}{11}$
$-\ 2\frac{1}{22}$

T. $14\frac{7}{12}$
$-\ 9\frac{1}{6}$

L. $6\frac{5}{12}$
$-\ 3\frac{2}{6}$

S. $12\frac{9}{14}$
$-\ 11\frac{2}{7}$

P. $7\frac{7}{9}$
$-\ 6\frac{1}{3}$

How does a mad scientist freshen his breath?

To find out, begin at Start and count one word for each circle while saying, "I will rule the world!" Every time you say the word *world,* write that circle's letter on the next line below.

__ __ __ __ __ " __ __ __ __ __ __ - __ __ __ __ __ "!

• Good, Clean Fun •

Subtract. Write each answer in simplest form. Then write each boxed number in the magic square. Each row and column should have a sum of 34.

A. $8\frac{5}{7}$
$-7\frac{1}{2}$

$1\frac{3}{\boxed{14}}$

B. $14\frac{10}{11}$
$-13\frac{13}{22}$

□

C. $54\frac{9}{12}$
$-51\frac{1}{3}$

□

D. $26\frac{5}{7}$
$-24\frac{9}{14}$

□

E. $18\frac{7}{9}$
$-17\frac{1}{6}$

□

F. $41\frac{5}{9}$
$-39\frac{1}{3}$

□

G. $3\frac{7}{9}$
$-1\frac{5}{12}$

□

H. $12\frac{7}{10}$
$-8\frac{1}{6}$

□

I. $20\frac{4}{6}$
$-19\frac{7}{15}$

□

J. $27\frac{7}{8}$
$-27\frac{3}{16}$

□

K. $8\frac{7}{11}$
$-8\frac{1}{2}$

□

L. $14\frac{3}{5}$
$-13\frac{1}{2}$

□

M. $20\frac{5}{12}$
$-19\frac{1}{6}$

□

N. $44\frac{11}{13}$
$-44\frac{1}{2}$

□

O. $9\frac{2}{3}$
$-7\frac{1}{2}$

□

P. $28\frac{2}{3}$
$-27\frac{2}{5}$

□

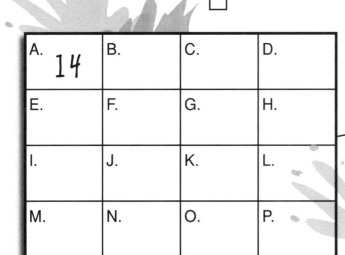

A. 14	B.	C.	D.
E.	F.	G.	H.
I.	J.	K.	L.
M.	N.	O.	P.

©The Mailbox® • *Math Practice Galore* • TEC61089 • Key p. 94

• Join the Club •

Subtract. Write the answer in simplest form in the puzzle.
The first one has been done for you.

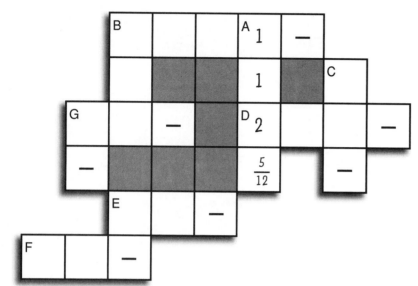

Down

A. $117\frac{2}{3}$
  $-\ 5\frac{1}{4}$
  $\overline{112\frac{5}{12}}$

B. $186\frac{2}{3}$
  $-15\frac{4}{6}$

C. $57\frac{4}{5}$
  $-\ 6\frac{3}{8}$

E. $10\frac{7}{8}$
  $-\ 8\frac{5}{10}$

G. $12\frac{3}{4}$
  $-11\frac{1}{2}$

Across

B. $1{,}604\frac{6}{10}$
  $-\ 353\frac{2}{5}$

D. $324\frac{4}{5}$
  $-\ 43\frac{15}{25}$

E. $36\frac{4}{6}$
  $-16\frac{1}{3}$

F. $25\frac{1}{2}$
  $-\ 8\frac{1}{8}$

G. $14\frac{5}{8}$
  $-\ 3\frac{6}{12}$

• Secret Passage •

Subtract. Write each answer in simplest form. Then color the answer in the maze to reveal the path.

A. $7\frac{1}{6}$
  $-\ 6\frac{2}{3}$

B. $5\frac{1}{4}$
  $-\ 4\frac{1}{3}$

C. $2\frac{1}{4}$
  $-\ 1\frac{3}{8}$

D. $7\frac{3}{8}$
  $-\ 6\frac{5}{8}$

E. $9\frac{2}{5}$
  $-\ 8\frac{3}{5}$

F. $8\frac{1}{10}$
  $-\ 7\frac{4}{5}$

G. $11\frac{1}{5}$
  $-\ 10\frac{3}{5}$

H. $4\frac{3}{8}$
  $-\ 3\frac{5}{8}$

I. $6\frac{1}{9}$
  $-\ 5\frac{1}{3}$

J. $3\frac{1}{7}$
  $-\ 2\frac{3}{14}$

Start

Maze values: $\frac{1}{2}$, $\frac{5}{9}$, $\frac{11}{12}$, $\frac{7}{8}$, $\frac{3}{4}$, $6\frac{1}{6}$, $2\frac{3}{4}$, $\frac{2}{3}$, $\frac{1}{6}$, $\frac{13}{14}$, $2\frac{1}{2}$, $\frac{4}{5}$, $\frac{3}{4}$, $\frac{10}{11}$, $4\frac{1}{8}$, $\frac{3}{5}$, $\frac{3}{10}$

NAME _____ DATE _____

•Jump Through Hoops •

Solve. Write each answer in simplest form. Then use
a ruler to draw a line to connect each problem number
with its answer. You will draw two lines for problems 1
and 12

1. $\begin{array}{r} 1 \\ -\ \frac{1}{5} \\ \hline \end{array}$

2. $\begin{array}{r} 2 \\ +\ \frac{1}{3} \\ \hline \end{array}$

3. $\begin{array}{r} 3 \\ -\ \frac{5}{6} \\ \hline \end{array}$

4. $\begin{array}{r} 2 \\ -\ \frac{1}{3} \\ \hline \end{array}$

5. $\begin{array}{r} 10 \\ -\ 3\frac{3}{9} \\ \hline \end{array}$

6. $\begin{array}{r} 2 \\ +\ 1\frac{7}{9} \\ \hline \end{array}$

7. $\begin{array}{r} 5 \\ +\ 3\frac{2}{3} \\ \hline \end{array}$

8. $\begin{array}{r} 3 \\ +\ 2\frac{1}{2} \\ \hline \end{array}$

9. $\begin{array}{r} 7 \\ +\ 2\frac{8}{9} \\ \hline \end{array}$

10. $\begin{array}{r} 3 \\ -\ 2\frac{6}{9} \\ \hline \end{array}$

11. $\begin{array}{r} 9 \\ -\ 3\frac{1}{3} \\ \hline \end{array}$

12. $\begin{array}{r} 1 \\ +\ \frac{11}{12} \\ \hline \end{array}$

• **Adding and subtracting mixed numbers** •

Don't Lose Your Marbles!

Multiply the two fractions pointing to an empty marble. Write your answer in simplest form in the empty marble.

$\frac{1}{3}$ $\frac{2}{3}$ $\frac{3}{5}$ $\frac{4}{7}$ $\frac{1}{2}$ $\frac{3}{4}$ $\frac{3}{7}$

• To the Top •

Multiply. Cut out each triangle at the bottom of the page. Match each problem to its product. Then glue the pieces in place.

$4\frac{1}{2} \times \frac{1}{2}$

$7 \times \frac{1}{5}$ $3 \times \frac{1}{6}$ $10\frac{1}{2} \times \frac{1}{5}$ $12 \times \frac{1}{4}$ $9 \times \frac{1}{6}$ $5 \times \frac{1}{3}$ $\frac{2}{4}$ $8\frac{1}{3} \times \frac{1}{3}$ $\frac{1}{2}$ $1\frac{1}{8}$ $1\frac{2}{5}$ $2\frac{1}{10}$ $1\frac{13}{18}$ $2\frac{7}{9}$ 3

$2 \times \frac{1}{3}$ $\frac{2}{3}$

• A Kingly Quest •

Why did the king go to the dentist?

Use a ruler to draw lines connecting matching fractions and decimals. Some numbers will not be used. Write the letters that do not have a line through them in order from left to right on the lines below.

0.7 •		• 0.06
$\frac{35}{100}$ •		• 0.35
0.52 •		• 0.1
$\frac{49}{1000}$ •		• 0.49
$\frac{15}{100}$ •		• $\frac{12}{100}$
$\frac{49}{100}$ •		• 0.15
$\frac{6}{10}$ •		• 0.6
0.12 •		• 0.8
$\frac{3}{10}$ •		• $\frac{7}{10}$
$\frac{8}{10}$ •		• $\frac{52}{100}$
$\frac{1}{10}$ •		• 0.3

T   N   A
   O
                T
      G
              E
   C   J
B   K
   H   S
      I
M   N   L   Q   S
              P
   T   E   T   W
 R   O   E   Y   H
U
      Z   O   Y   X
   C   R   V   I   O
 M
        W   N
        F
              E   T
                 D

___ ___ ___ ___   ___ ___ ___ ___ ___ ___ ___   ___ ___ ___ ___ ___!

NAME_____ DATE _____

· What's for Lunch? ·

2 in the hundredths place	4 in the tenths place	2 in the tenths place	4 in the hundredths place
5 in the tenths place	1 in the hundredths place	9 in the tenths place	5 in the hundredths place
9 in the hundredths place	8 in the tenths place	7 in the hundredths place	8 in the hundredths place
7 in the tenths place	6 in the hundredths place	1 in the tenths place	6 in the tenths place

Cut out the answer boxes. Glue each box to its matching space in the grid to create a picture that answers the question.

©The Mailbox® · *Math Practice Galore* · TEC61089 · Key p. 95

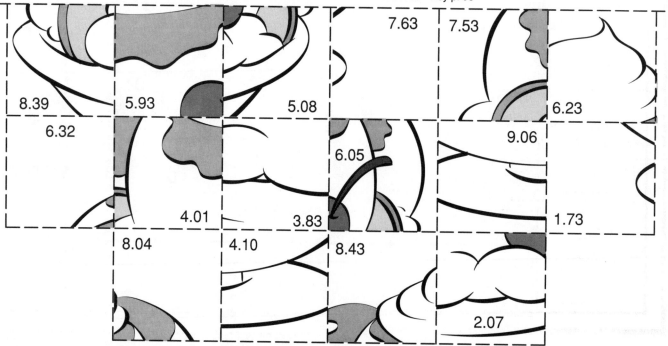

7.63   7.53

8.39   5.93   5.08   6.23

6.32   9.06

6.05

4.01   3.83   1.73

8.04   4.10   8.43

2.07

• Words for the Wise •

Find the number in the key that matches each clue. Write the letter of your answer in the space provided. If you are correct, your answers will form a word in each row and column.

Puzzle 1

1 in the thousandths place	1 in the hundredths place	3 in the tenths place
_____	_____	_____
9 in the hundredths place		3 in the thousandths place
_____		_____
3 in the hundredths place	9 in the thousandths place	1 in the tenths place
_____	_____	_____

Key for Puzzle 1

26.214 = U	8.971 = M
72.358 = D	40.273 = O
19.145 = G	53.636 = T
0.794 = A	10.079 = U

Puzzle 2

5 in the hundredths place	2 in the thousandths place	7 in the tenths place
_____	_____	_____
5 in the thousandths place		9 in the tenths place
_____		_____
2 in the tenths place	5 in the tenths place	2 in the hundredths place
_____	_____	_____

Key for Puzzle 2

51.933 = A	61.548 = I
39.268 = D	9.056 = N
4.872 = E	12.115 = O
7.123 = G	6.749 = T

NAME_____ DATE_____

Circle the correct comparisons. To find the path up the mountain, connect the circles from the bottom to the top.

Which mountain sleeps all the time?
To answer the question, write the circled letters in order from start to finish on the lines below.

___ ___ ___ ___ ___ ___   ___ ___ ___ ___ ___ ___ ___

Finish

T.
1.01 < 1.10

S.
0.457 > 0.364

E.
7.37 < 7.39

U.
1.11 < 1.10

C.
4.567 > 4.657

R.
0.72 > 0.702

B.
1.77 < 1.75

E.
2.47 < 2.54

V.
0.494 < 0.495

E.
0.499 < 0.500

L.
7.117 < 7.107

T.
2.17 > 2.07

N.
0.512 < 5.21

S.
3.67 < 3.07

I.
5.455 > 5.545

S.
5.614 > 5.641

W.
1.621 < 1.612

U.
0.189 > 0.109

O.
0.009 < 0.107

M.
6.409 > 6.403

Start

• Showing the Way •

Connect the
decimals in order from
least to greatest.

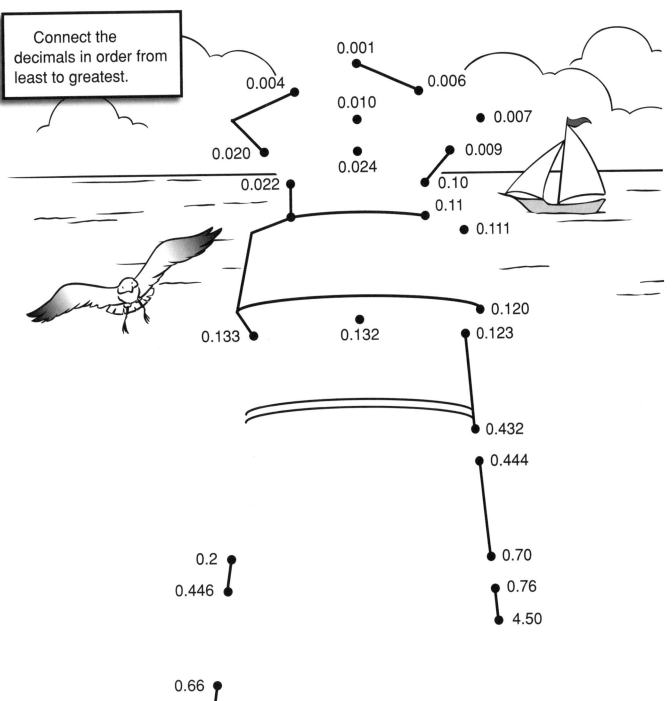

0.001

0.004

0.006

0.010

0.007

0.020

0.024

0.009

0.022

0.10

0.11

0.111

0.120

0.123

0.133

0.132

0.432

0.444

0.70

0.2

0.76

0.446

4.50

0.66

2.03

2.13

2.23

2.21

2.22

Branching Out

Round each number to the nearest whole number. Write each answer in its matching box. If you are correct, the sum of each row, column, and diagonal on a house will equal the number on its roof.

A.	1.9 ≈ _____	B.	16.23 ≈ _____
C.	12.55 ≈ _____	D.	21.78 ≈ _____
E.	35.06 ≈ _____	F.	4.9 ≈ _____
G.	9.74 ≈ _____	H.	22.51 ≈ _____
I.	3.49 ≈ _____	J.	9.39 ≈ _____
K.	12.01 ≈ _____	L.	10.88 ≈ _____
M.	34.09 ≈ _____	N.	14.88 ≈ _____
O.	13.67 ≈ _____		

House — 34

B	3	2	C
5	G	11	8
J	6	7	K
4	N	O	1

House — 15

A	7	6
9	F	1
4	I	8

House — 69

D	12	E
36	H	10
L	M	24

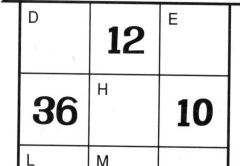

Oh, My Stars!

Round each number to the underlined place value. Write your answer in the puzzle, using one number or decimal from each column below. Then cross out each number or decimal used.

A. 5.0$\underline{6}$2   =

B. 11.7$\underline{6}$7   =

C. 10.6$\underline{7}$9   =

D. 1.7$\underline{7}$7   =

E. 601.$\underline{6}$7   =

F. 0.$\underline{5}$9   =

G. 3.$\underline{0}$6   =

H. 379.$\underline{1}$9   =

I. 0.$\underline{2}$47   =

J. 21.$\underline{1}$4   =

5	.		☆	■
				☆
				☆
			☆	■
				☆
		☆	■	■
		☆	■	■
			☆	■
		☆	■	■
			☆	■

6	0	2	7	2
3	✕	.	.	8
1	1	1	6	7
✕	.	.	6	7
1	.	.		8
0	1	0	.	
2	0	6	1	
3	7	7		
1	.	1		
0	.	9		

Write each starred digit from above in its matching star below. If you are correct, you'll form a number that reads the same backward or forward.

A ☆ , J ☆ E ☆ H ☆ , D ☆ C ☆ I ☆ , B ☆ G ☆ F ☆

Number Pyramids

1. | 77.6 | | 20.1 |

2. | 33.58 | | 44.34 |

3. | 55.39 | | 37.2 |

4. | 2.8 | | 56.3 |

5. | 77.52 | | 14.29 |

6. | 719.07 | | 91.41 |

7. | 41.43 | | 6.85 |

8. | 25.8 | | 3.0 |

9. | 26.85 | | 61.33 |

10. | 17.0 | | 1.3 |

11. | 63.395 | | 20.061 |

12. | 33.975 | | 22.495 |

Add the decimals in the lower boxes. Write the sums in the upper boxes. If your answers are correct, the last two digits of one sum will be the first two digits of the next sum.

• A Hamster's Home •

Add. Write your answers in the puzzle.

7.431 + 9.697 = _____   49.809

3.79 + 51.9 = _____   + 53.496 =

7.58 + _____ =   81.4

8.51   47.49 + 89.6 = _____   2.357 + 6.617 = _____

9.888   6.61 + 4.04 = _____

5.874 + 0.632

54.94 + 0.979 = _____

Molecule Math

Subtract. If your answers are correct, the sum of the answers along each diagonal will be the same.

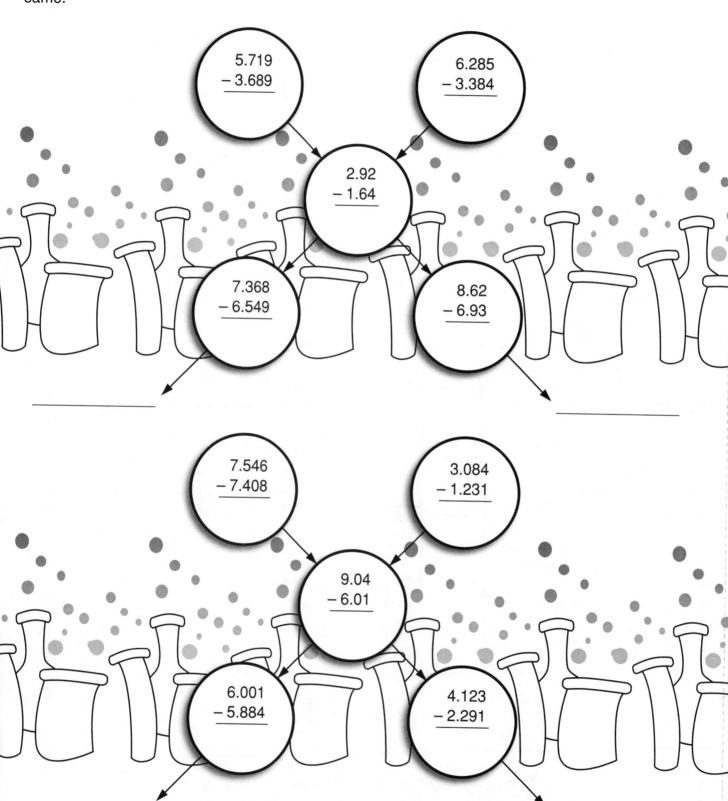

$$5.719 - 3.689$$

$$6.285 - 3.384$$

$$2.92 - 1.64$$

$$7.368 - 6.549$$

$$8.62 - 6.93$$

$$7.546 - 7.408$$

$$3.084 - 1.231$$

$$9.04 - 6.01$$

$$6.001 - 5.884$$

$$4.123 - 2.291$$

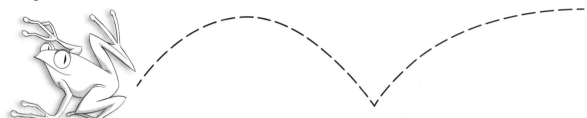

An "A-maze-ing" Maze

Subtract. Circle each problem that has been solved correctly. Connect the circled problems to find the way through the maze.

Start

$2.12 - 0.494 = 1.637$

$0.236 - 0.097 = 0.139$

$4.26 - 0.75 = 3.51$

$0.812 - 0.785 = 0.027$

$$\begin{array}{r} 0.154 \\ -\ 0.099 \\ \hline 0.155 \end{array}$$

$2.753 - 0.485 = 2.268$

$7.76 - 1.43 = 6.39$

$5.723 - 5.649 = 0.074$

$5.83 - 0.84 = 4.89$

$3.05 - 2.02 = 1.03$

$1.41 - 0.23 = 1.08$

$0.622 - 0.256 = 0.466$

$1.234 - 0.567 = 0.667$

$1.183 - 0.778 = 0.415$

$6.1 - 5.7 = 0.4$

$0.544 - 0.456 = 0.098$

$9.347 - 2.381 = 6.865$

$3.07 - 2.48 = 0.58$

$0.022 - 0.009 = 0.012$

$3.354 - 2.999 = 0.355$

Finish

• Making Loops •

Circle the two numbers in a row, column, or diagonal that equal each given product when multiplied. If you are correct, the sum of all the circled numbers will equal 89.8.

1. product of 4

0.05	8
5	0.5

2. product of 2.4

1.02	2
12	0.2

3. product of 0.6

0.02	0.6
1	3

4. product of 4.4

11	0.02
2	0.4

5. product of 3

10	0.3
15	0.02

6. product of 18.4

9	2.2
2.3	8

7. product of 42

0.21	10.5
2	4

8. product of 29.4

4.2	6
7	0.7

9. product of 15.6

5.3	7.8
3	2

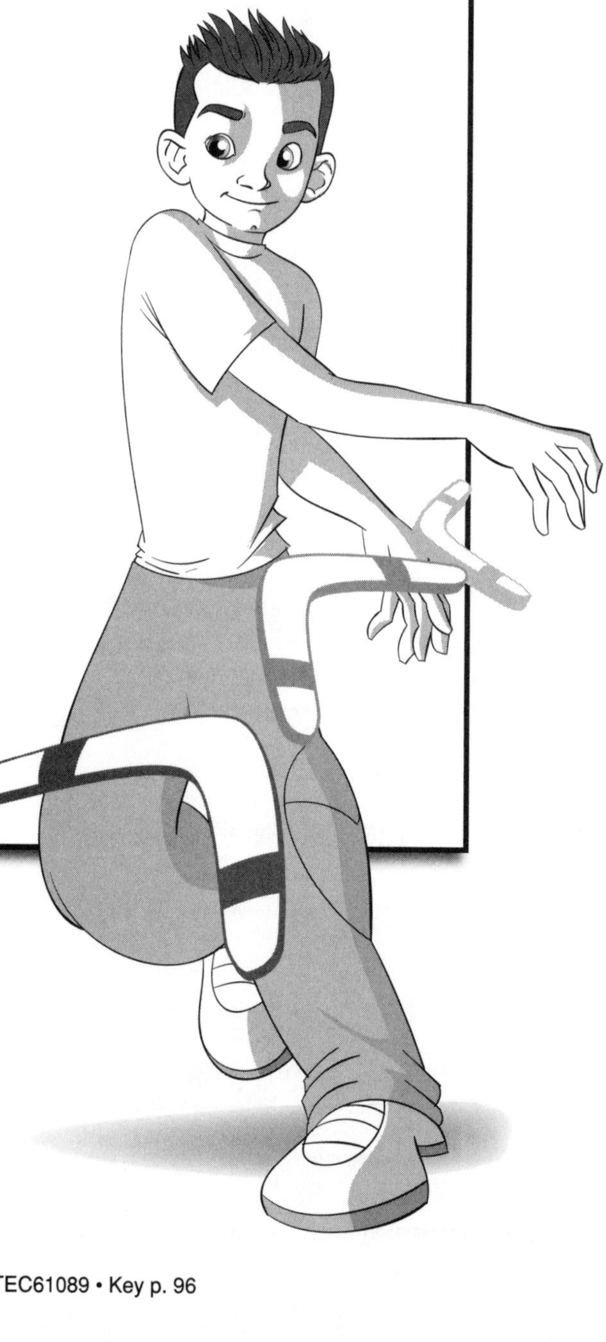

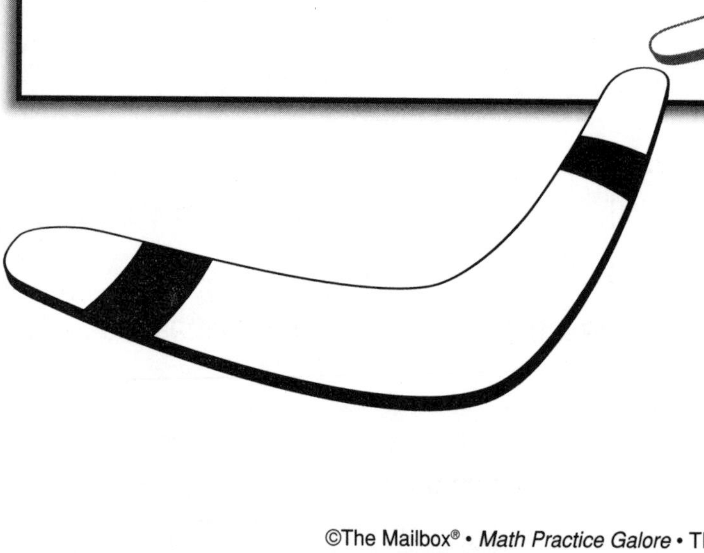

• Crack the Code! •

Use the code to multiply.

Code
👽 = 1	🛸 = 3	⬅ = 5	◸ = 7	✋ = 9
✦ = 2	🧍 = 4	🌀 = 6	✕ = 8	∞ = 0

M. 👽 . 🌀
   x   🧍
   _____

W. ⬅ . ⬅ ✕
   x   ◸
   _____

L. ∞ . 🧍 ✋ 🌀
   x   ✕
   _____

E. ✦ 👽 . ✕
   x   ✋
   _____

R. 👽 🌀 . 🧍 🛸
   x   ⬅
   _____

S. ◸ . ∞ 👽 ✕
   x   🌀
   _____
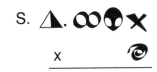

L. 🛸 🌀 . ✦
   x   🛸
   _____

N. 🧍 . ⬅ 👽 🧍
   x   ✦
   _____

O. ⬅ 🌀 . 👽 ✕
   x   🌀
   _____

On July 8, 1947, William Brazel and a United States Army Air Force officer said a UFO had crashed in the United States. The military later said it was not a UFO but was a weather balloon.

Where did this famous UFO sighting take place?

To answer the question, write each letter from above on its matching numbered line below.

_____ _____ _____ _____ _____ _____ _____, _____ _____
82.15 337.08 42.108 39.06 196.2 108.6 3.968   9.028 6.4

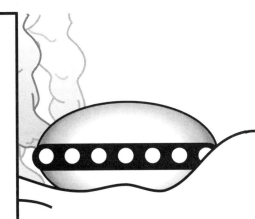

A Triangular Trail

For each triangle, write in the circles the numbers whose products equal the numbers in the boxes between them. Use the number bank to help you. Some of the triangles have been started for you.

Number Bank

0.3	0.7	1.82	2.9	~~5.7~~
0.4	0.75	2.4	~~4.1~~	5.8
0.44	0.98	2.5	4.9	8.8
	1.5	~~2.6~~	5.5	

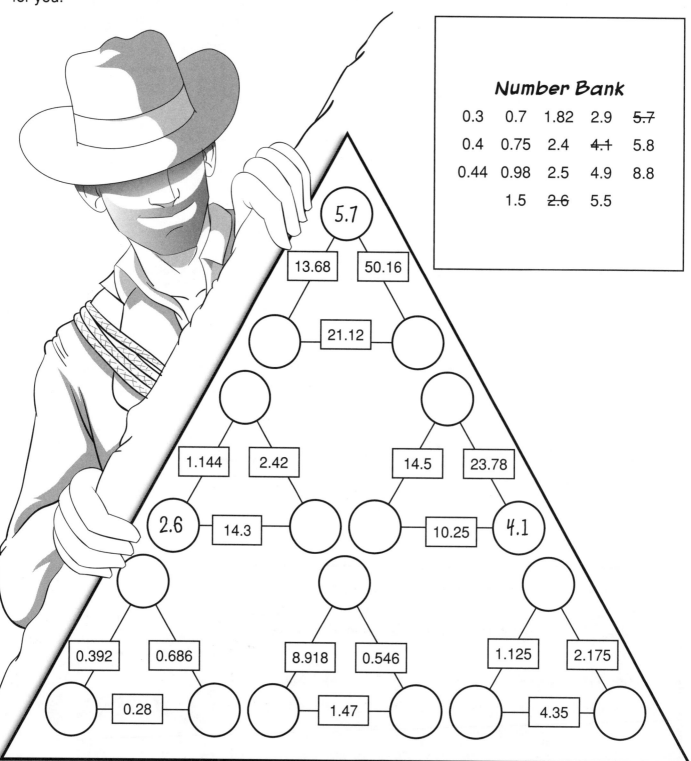

• Sail On! •

Multiply. Write the products in the puzzle. The first one has been done for you.

Across

A. 6.3
   x 0.4

   2.52

D. 7.68
   x 1.9

F. 1.3
   x 2.7

H. 0.56
   x 0.4

J. 4.25
   x 1.3

K. 24.6
   x 1.9

Down

B. 8.7
   x 6.3

C. 7.09
   x 0.6

D. 2.3
   x 7.2

E. 7.2
   x 3.4

G. 6.41
   x 0.9

I. 18.06
   x 2.5

• Messenger Boy •

Divide. Write the quotients in the grid. If your answers are correct, the sum of each row and column will equal 6.5.

A] 4.5 ÷ 3 = _____

B] 6.4 ÷ 4 = _____

C] 17.6 ÷ 8 = _____

D] 3.3 ÷ 11 = _____

E] 5.6 ÷ 4 = _____

F] 16.0 ÷ 8 = _____

G] 14.7 ÷ 7 = _____

H] 2.1 ÷ 3 = _____

I] 11.4 ÷ 6 = _____

J] 4.5 ÷ 9 = _____

K] 2.4 ÷ 4 = _____

L] 5.4 ÷ 3 = _____

M] 11.5 ÷ 5 = _____

N] 2.8 ÷ 7 = _____

O] 9.0 ÷ 9 = _____

A.	B.	C.	D. 0.9
0.8	E.	F.	G. 0.2
0.1	H.	I. 1.3	2.5
2.4	J.	K.	L. 1.2
1.7	M.	N.	O. 1.1

©The Mailbox® • Math Practice Galore • TEC61089 • Key p. 96

Answer Keys

Page 4

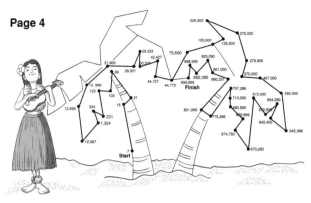

Page 8

A. 6,020	F. 11,231	D. 10,111
H. 13,120	E. 10,321	C. 6,633
I. 14,522	B. 6,021	G. 11,963
J. 15,061		

6 0 2 0	6 0 2 1	6 6 3 3	1 0 1 1 1	1 0 3 2 1
A	B	C	D	E

1 1 2 3 1	1 1 9 6 3	1 3 1 2 0	1 4 5 2 2	1 5 0 6 1
F	G	H	I	J

Page 5

A. six millions
B. six hundred thousands
C. six millions
D. six tens
E. six tens
F. six hundreds
G. six thousands

Page 6

A. 5,222	B. 2,482	C. 7,312	D. 9,404
E. 9,722	F. 4,607	G. 2,300	H. 7,530
I. 9,741	J. 10,234	K. 2,860	L. 5,380

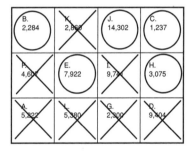

Page 7

Paths may vary.

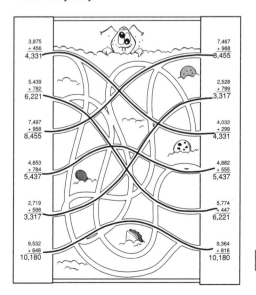

Page 9

A. 4,860	B. 8,699
C. 13,932	D. 5,364
E. 4,255	F. 6,825
G. 13,643	H. 4,759
I. 9,876	J. 6,083

Page 10

Across
A. 6,684
C. 8,749
D. 8,789
F. 2,246
I. 3,745

Down
B. 4,848
C. 8,488
E. 7,575
G. 9,279
H. 4,836

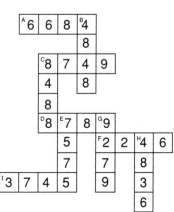

Page 11

A. 6,569
B. 5,889
C. 4,887
D. 3,888
E. 2,779
F. 3,358
G. 2,737
H. 6,782
I. 5,784
J. 4,319
K. 2,809
L. 1,089

LONG TIME NO "SEA"!

Page 12

A. 3,328
B. 1,509
C. 5,085
D. 2,284
E. 479
F. 2,528
G. 8,639
H. 7,127
I. 1,127
J. 3,196
K. 6,472
L. 2,376

1	3	5	6	7	5	3	2	2	8	4
1	5	0	9	2	1	2	5	1	9	7
2	0	7	6	3	7	1	2	5	2	4
7	8	8	9	4	4	5	8	6	3	9
2	5	4	4	7	4	7	2	1	2	5
1	3	3	2	8	8	2	9	2	6	3
4	6	3	1	9	6	9	0	4	3	2

Page 13

A. 3,461
B. 3,454
C. 3,459
D. 3,456
E. 3,458
F. 3,460
G. 3,457
H. 3,462
I. 3,455

10,374

Page 16

A. 508   B. 832
C. 2,016   D. 6,363
E. 3,815   F. 5,872
G. 2,465   H. 5,004
I. 4,795   J. 5,856

Page 17

1. 876   2. 784   3. 5,800
4. 1,326   5. 1,887   6. 6,840
7. 1,325   8. 1,432   9. 2,958
10. 1,585   11. 2,541   12. 4,040

Page 14

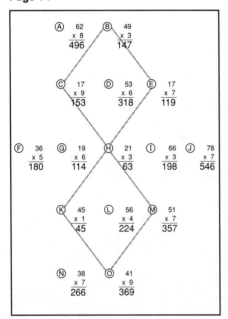

Page 15

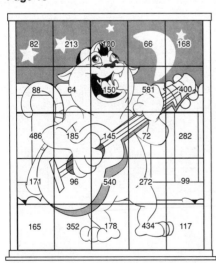

Page 18

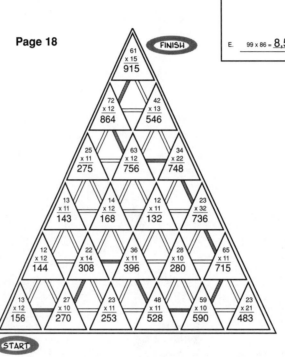

Page 19

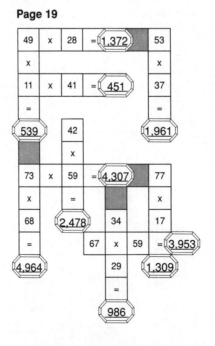

Page 20

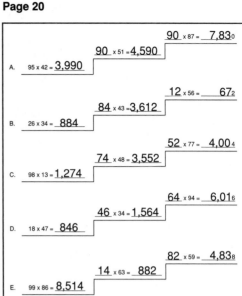

Page 21

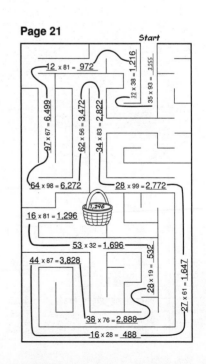

Page 22

A. 299 B. 2,349 C. 1,827 D. 4,656
E. 1,196 F. 4,680 G. 3,024 H. 8,051
I. 1,365 J. 3,588 K. 2,464 L. 966

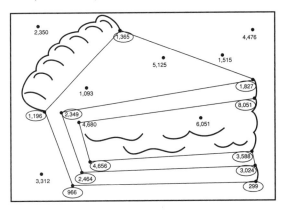

Page 23

246 × 19 = 4,674
604 × 31 = 18,724
452 × 46 = 20,792
631 × 20 = 12,620
577 × 46 = 26,542
286 × 25 = 7,150
664 × 34 = 22,576
20,560
214 × 57 = 12,198
168 × 52 = 8,736
283 × 47 = 13,301

Page 24

840 × 25 = 21,000
829 × 54 = 44,766
255 × 49 = 12,495
612 × 27 = 16,524
138 × 15 = 2,070
268 × 36 = 9,648
494 × 11 = 5,434
315 × 51 = 16,065
678 × 43 = 29,154
151 × 72 = 10,872

	1	5	9	4	8	6	8	9	1	
0	3	6	1	0	8	7	2	7	8	6	5	1
1	5	4	2	3	9	2	9	1	5	4	6
8	9	6	0	1	4	4	7	6	6	3	7
1	3	7	8	0	2	9	1	3	5	2	4	8
1	0	1	6	0	6	5	5	4	2	0	9	1
3	4	5	0	1	7	9	6	4	8	0

Page 25

							A2	8	7	7	0
	B7			C5	0	7	6
D1	7	6	3	2		1		5
	2		9			9		E9	9	F3	3
	4		G2	7	2	3	2		5		8
	2		5							7
	7								5

Across
A. 28,770
C. 5,076
D. 17,632
E. 9,933
G. 27,232

Down
A. 26,595
B. 76,925
C. 5,192
D. 12,427
F. 3,875

Page 26

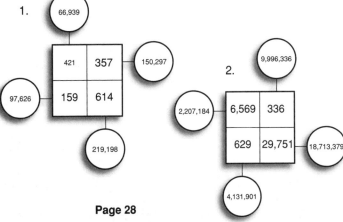

72,152 318,150 586,040
220,317 2,137,424
298,100
306,450 55,632 339,690 1,178,338

Page 27

1.
66,939
421 | 357
159 | 614
150,297
97,626
219,198

2.
9,996,336
6,569 | 336
629 | 29,751
2,207,184
18,713,379
4,131,901

Page 28

A. 8,000 H. 6,000
B. 24,000 I. 9,000
C. 5,000 J. 15,000
D. 10,000 K. 4,000
E. 40,000 L. 7,200
F. 12,000 M. 7,000
G. 18,000

8,000	24,000	5,000	10,000	40,000	12,000	18,000	6,000	9,000	15,000	4,000	7,200	7,000
W	H	A	T		D	I	D		T	H	E	
G	A	R	D	E	N	E	R		S	A	Y	
T	O		T	H	E		F	L	O	W	E	R
T	H	A	T		W	A	S		N	O	T	
G	R	O	W	I	N	G	?		W	H	A	T
A		L	A	Z	Y		D	A	I	S	Y	!

Page 29

A. 2,000
B. 7,000
C. 2,000
D. 7,000
E. 4,000
F. 3,000
G. 4,000
H. 3,000
I. 6,000
J. 1,000
K. 6,000
L. 1,000
M. 4,000
N. 5,000
O. 4,000
P. 5,000

Sum of the products on each slice = 8,000

Page 30

1. 16
2. 7
3. 12
4. 13
5. 6
6. 10
7. 39
8. 13
9. 8
10. 33
11. 9
12. 7
13. 7
14. 2
15. 23
16. 34
17. 8
18. 19
19. 6
20. 9

Page 31

1. 22, WHA
2. 6, TTY
3. 47, PEO
4. 14, FSA
5. 15, NDW
6. 4, ICH
7. 17, WOU
8. 5, LDA
9. 12, SHA
10. 44, RKOR
11. 24, DER
12. 8, IFIT
13. 11, WENT
14. 10, TOADI
15. 13, NER?

¹W	H	A	²T		T	Y	³P	E		O	F		S	A	⁵N	D	W	⁶I	C	H	
⁷W	O	U	⁸L	D		A		⁹S	H	A	¹⁰R	K		O	R	D	¹¹E	R			
¹²I	F		I	T		¹³W	E	N	T		¹⁴T	O		A			¹⁵D	I	N	E	R	?

Page 32

Across
A. 3 R4
C. 5 R3
E. 4 R3
F. 2 R2
G. 19 R1
H. 1 R7
J. 21 R1
K. 23 R2

Down
A. 3 R2
B. 45 R1
D. 3 R2
E. 42 R1
I. 7 R1
J. 2 R2
K. 2 R5

```
ᴬ3  R  ᴮ4        ᶜ5  R  ᴰ3
R      5         R      ᴱ4  R  3
2      R         ᶠ2  R  2
       ᴳ1  9  R  1      R
                        ᴴ1  R  ᴵ7
                        R
                 ᴶ2  1  R  1
                 R
            ᴷ2  3  R  2
            R
            5
```

Page 33

1. 22 R2; Because it works for chicken <u>feed</u>!
2. 9 R3; They go on "<u>peck-nics</u>"!
3. 11 R5; "<u>Fry-day</u>"!
4. 9 R2; It was a <u>rubber chicken</u>!
5. 11 R2; It was a "<u>hen-velope</u>"!
6. 5 R8; <u>Around the "cluck"</u>!
7. 28 R1; He was <u>chicken</u>!
8. 5 R2; To get to the <u>other slide</u>!
9. 24 R3; "<u>Comedi-hens</u>"!
10. 8 R2; <u>From scratch</u>!

Page 34

1. 153 R1
2. 79 R1
3. 31 R5
4. 97 R2
5. 141 R2
6. 45 R8
7. 154 R4
8. 64 R1
9. 58 R2
10. 118 R1

Page 35

A. $4)\overline{261}$ = 65 R1

B. $6)\overline{519}$ = 86 R3

C. $9)\overline{705}$ = 78 R3

D. $5)\overline{343}$ = 68 R3

E. $2)\overline{425}$ = 212 R1

F. $7)\overline{860}$ = 122 R6

G. $3)\overline{299}$ = 99 R2

H. $6)\overline{847}$ = 141 R1

The thief is
<u>Fearless Fran</u>.

Page 36

A. 308
B. 107 R3
C. 204 R3
D. 80 R2
E. 407 R1
F. 70 R4
G. 208 R3
H. 107 R1
I. 205 R2
J. 105 R4
K. 50 R2
L. 90 R4

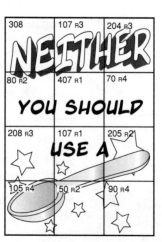

Page 37

Start
107 R1 2)215
140 R4 5)704
91 R2 7)639
56 R4 6)340
147 2)294
30 R6 7)216
108 9)972
24 R2 9)218
108 R3 8)867
70 R5 6)425
112 7)784
107 R1 4)429
113 R3 5)568
110 R6 9)996
196 R2 3)590
114 R1 6)685
104 R7 9)839
209 2)418
Finish

Page 38

	Quotient		Remainder
A.	17	17	0
B.	53	63	10
C.	16	38	22
D.	11	13	2
E.	25	40	15
F.	21	21	0
G.	19	30	11
H.	15	39	24
I.	25	38	13
J.	29	31	2

Page 39

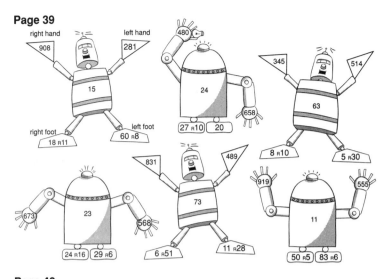

Page 40

A. 235 R8
B. 80 R6
C. 675 R4
D. 43 R23
E. 31 R16
F. 62 R58
G. 819 R2
H. 21 R2
I. 26 R33
J. 35 R23

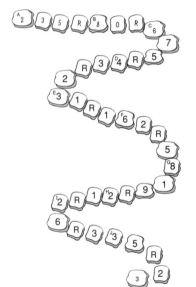

Page 41

1. WHA 155 R30
2. TIS 221 R7
3. LIG 114 R7
4. HTB 83 R5
5. UTCA 46 R22
6. NNOT 128 R18
7. BEHE 74 R27
8. LDFO 32 R5
9. RLO 94 R84
10. NG? 135 R39

¹W	H	A	²T		I	S		³L	I	G	⁴H	T
B	⁵U	T			C	A	⁶N	N	O	T		⁷B	E
H	⁸E	L	D			F	O	⁹R		¹⁰L	O	N	G	?

Page 42

A. 203 R3
B. 40 R7
C. 350 R5
D. 660 R8
E. 206 R6
F. 109 R2
G. 401 R1
H. 80 R4
I. 70 R9

D. 8	A. 3	H. 4
G. 1	C. 5	I. 9
E. 6	B. 7	F. 2

Page 43

A. 101 R11
B. 60 R5
C. 207 R6
D. 50 R12
E. 280 R4
F. 40 R10
G. 407 R8
H. 400 R9
I. 50 R7

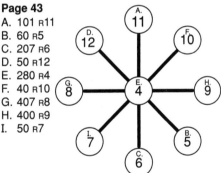

Page 44

Left Field ≈ 60
Center Field ≈ 40
Right Field ≈ 20
Third Base ≈ 30
Shortstop ≈ 50
Second Base ≈ 70
First Base ≈ 90
Pitcher ≈ 30
Catcher ≈ 10

Page 45

A. 30
B. 20
C. 50
D. 10
E. 40
F. 60
G. 70
H. 80

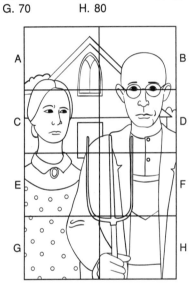

Page 46

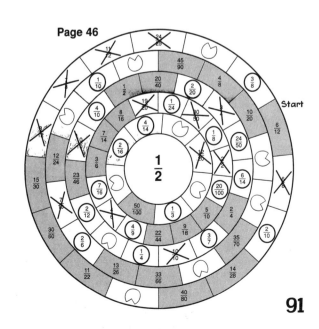

91

Page 47

Across
A. 12
B. 63
C. 30
F. 60
I. 56
J. 60
K. 33

Down
A. 20
D. 75
E. 40
G. 36
H. 18

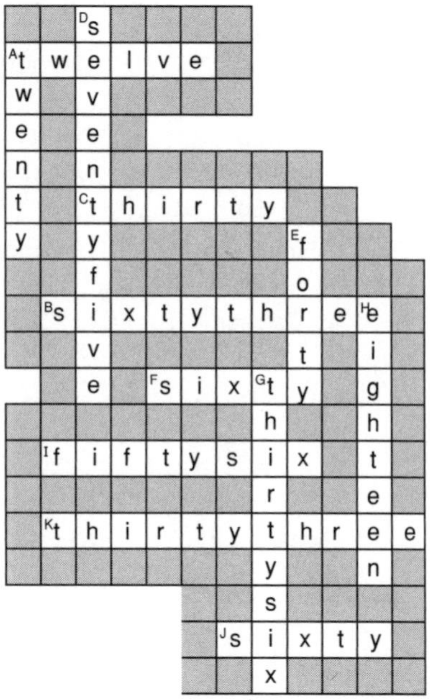

twelve
thirty
sixtythree
sixty
fiftysix
thirtythree
sixty
twenty
seventyfive
forty
thirtysix
eighteen

Page 48

A. 10
B. 12
C. 8
D. 15
E. 9
F. 6
G. 10
H. 9
I. 11
J. 5
K. 14
L. 11

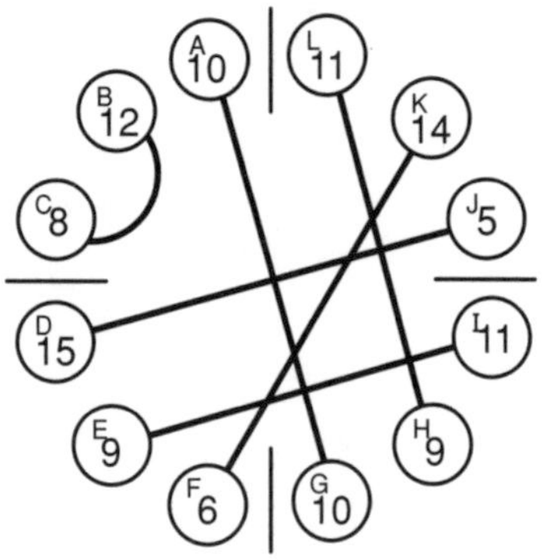

A 10
L 11
B 12
K 14
C 8
J 5
D 15
I 11
E 9
H 9
F 6
G 10

Page 49

A. ¾ B. ¼ C. ⅔ D. ⅔
E. ⅔ F. ½ G. ½ H. ½
I. ¼ J. ¼ K. ¾ L. ¾

¼	A ¾	F ½	⅔
E ⅔	H ½	L ¾	B ¼
K ¾	C ⅔	J ¼	G ½
½	I ¼	D ⅔	¾

Page 50

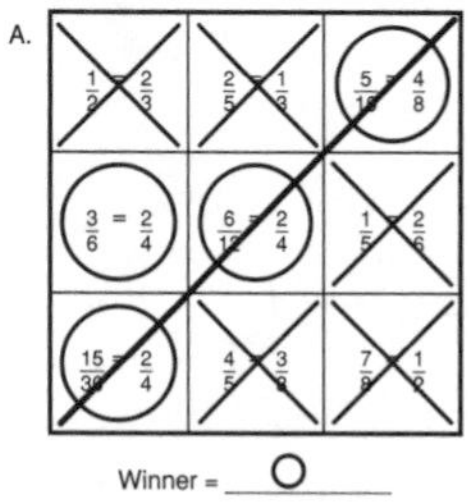

A.
Winner = O

"MAGMA-zines"

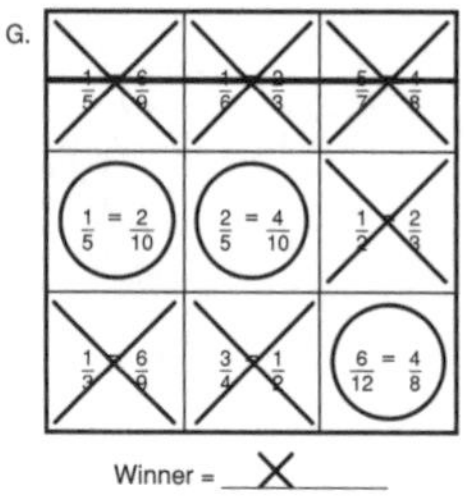

G.
Winner = X

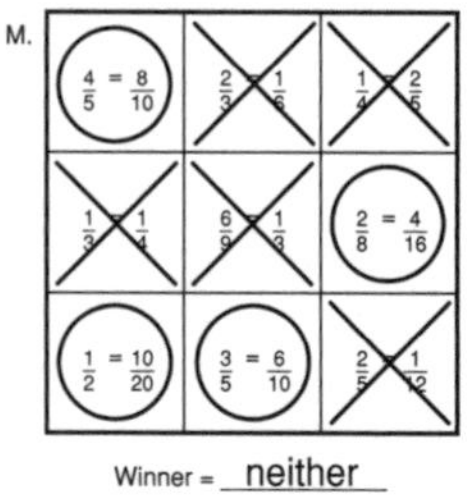

M.
Winner = neither

Page 51

1. WHA 2. TDO 3. YOU
4. CAL 5. LAH 6. AP
7. PY 8. CO
9. WB 10. OY

1 W	H	A	2 T		D	O		3 Y	O	U	
4 C	A	L	5 L		A		H	6 A	P	7 P	Y
	8 C	O	9 W	B	10 O	Y	?				

Page 52

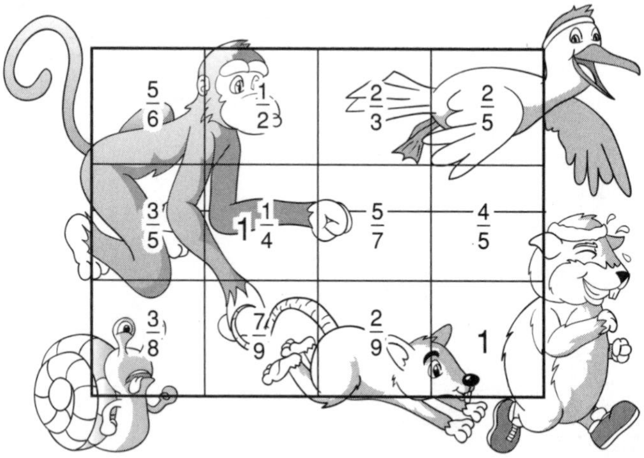

5/6
1/2
2/3
2/5
3/5
1 1/4
5/7
4/5
3/8
7/9
2/9
1

Page 53

A. ⅞ B. 9⁄10 C. 7⁄12 D. 11⁄12
E. ¾ F. ⅚
G. ⅝ H. ½

7/8	W	9/10 H	7/12 E	11/12 R	E	3/4	5/6 D	5/8 O	1/2	
M	I	L	K		S	H	A	K	E	S
C	O	M	E		F	R	O	M	?	
		N	E	R	V	O	U	S		
			C	O	W	S	!			

Page 54

A. 7⁄10
B. 31⁄35
C. 19⁄24
D. 23⁄24
E. 17⁄30
F. 13⁄36
G. ⅚
H. 7⁄9
I. 5⁄12
J. 7⁄10

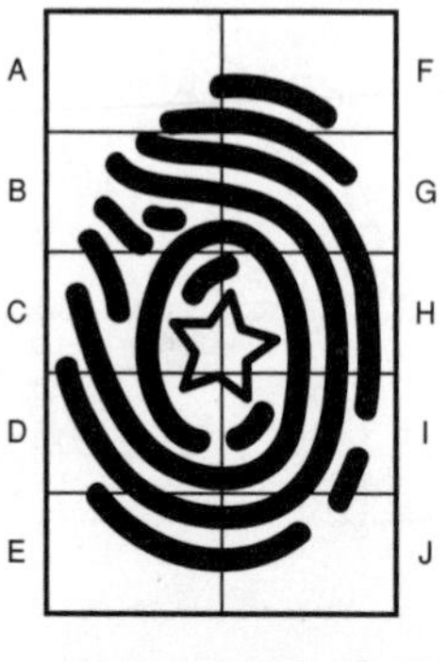

A
B
C
D
E
F
G
H
I
J

Page 55

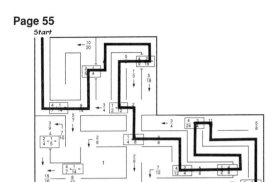

Page 56

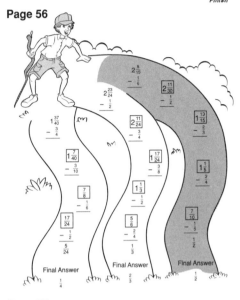

Page 59

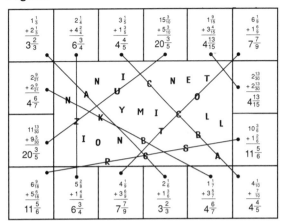

More than <u>NINETY MILLION</u> pounds!

Page 60

1. 4   "Bee-hive" yourself!
2. $5\frac{3}{8}$ A <u>bee flying backward</u>!
3. $1\frac{3}{7}$ A <u>queen bee</u>
4. $1\frac{1}{9}$ A <u>mumble bee</u>
5. $2\frac{2}{11}$ A <u>maybe</u>
6. $3\frac{1}{4}$ A <u>fumble bee</u>
7. $1\frac{2}{11}$ Because <u>they don't know</u> the <u>words</u>!
8. $1\frac{1}{5}$ A <u>spelling bee</u>
9. $6\frac{1}{12}$ Because <u>they have honey combs</u>!
10. $\frac{2}{7}$ On <u>a school "buzz"</u>!

Page 61

A	1	7		5	/	9	
B	7		9	/	1	0	
C	2	2		2	1	/	2	2
D	4		9	/	1	0	
E	8		7	9			
F	1	8		3	/	4	
G	5		1	1	/	1	4
H	1	8		1	7	/	2	0
I	2	0		1	5	/	2	2
★	3	0,	0	0	0,	0	0	0

Page 57

A. $\frac{4}{10} = \frac{2}{5}$ B. $\frac{12}{16} = \frac{3}{4}$ C. $\frac{2}{12} = \frac{1}{6}$

D. $\frac{9}{24} = \frac{3}{8}$ E. 0   F. $\frac{2}{14} = \frac{1}{7}$

G. $\frac{6}{10} = \frac{3}{5}$ H. $\frac{8}{10} = \frac{4}{5}$ I. $\frac{1}{9}$ J. $\frac{3}{6} = \frac{1}{2}$ K. $\frac{2}{10} = \frac{1}{5}$ L. $\frac{3}{24} = \frac{1}{8}$

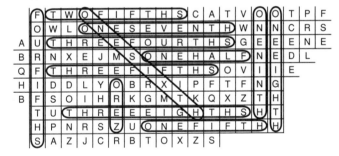

Page 58

START		
$\frac{7}{8}$ $-\frac{1}{6}$ $\frac{17}{24}$	$\frac{3}{4}$ $-\frac{1}{3}$ $\frac{5}{12}$	$\frac{11}{12}$ $-\frac{1}{5}$ $\frac{42}{60}$
	$\frac{6}{10}$ $-\frac{1}{5}$ $\frac{2}{5}$	$\frac{8}{9}$ $-\frac{1}{4}$ $\frac{23}{36}$
$\frac{4}{5}$ $-\frac{1}{3}$ $\frac{7}{15}$	$\frac{9}{11}$ $-\frac{2}{3}$ $\frac{5}{33}$	$\frac{7}{9}$ $-\frac{1}{3}$ $\frac{1}{3}$	$\frac{3}{4}$ $-\frac{1}{5}$ $\frac{11}{20}$
$\frac{9}{10}$ $-\frac{1}{4}$ $\frac{13}{20}$	$\frac{9}{12}$ $-\frac{1}{2}$ $\frac{1}{3}$	$\frac{5}{6}$ $-\frac{1}{2}$ $\frac{1}{3}$	$\frac{5}{7}$ $-\frac{1}{14}$ $\frac{4}{7}$
$\frac{6}{7}$ $-\frac{3}{8}$ $\frac{25}{56}$	$\frac{3}{4}$ $-\frac{1}{3}$ $\frac{7}{12}$	$\frac{6}{8}$ $-\frac{1}{3}$ $\frac{11}{24}$	$\frac{5}{9}$ $-\frac{1}{3}$ $\frac{3}{9}$
	FINISH	

Page 62

<u>WHY DO FIREFIGHTERS WEAR RED SUSPENDERS?</u>

D. $1\frac{5}{6}$ S. $13\frac{7}{12}$

E. $7\frac{5}{6}$ N. $13\frac{4}{7}$

H. $3\frac{13}{16}$ W. $15\frac{7}{12}$

F. $12\frac{1}{2}$ R. $7\frac{11}{12}$

P. $11\frac{13}{18}$ Y. $12\frac{7}{8}$

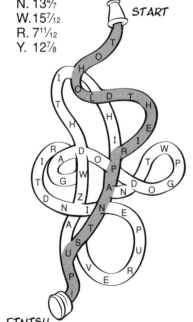

Page 63

A. $12\frac{9}{10}$
B. $11\frac{13}{24}$
C. $33\frac{8}{9}$
D. $19\frac{17}{18}$
E. $11\frac{27}{28}$
F. $15\frac{19}{30}$
G. $21\frac{7}{8}$
H. $10\frac{11}{15}$

A. twelve and nine-tenths
B. eleven and thirteen twenty-fourths
C. thirty-three and eight-ninths
D. nineteen and seventeen-eighteenths
E. eleven and twenty-seven twenty-eighths
F. fifteen and nineteen-thirtieths
G. twenty-one and seven-eighths
H. ten and eleven-fifteenths

Page 64

W. $4\frac{3}{8}$ X. $1\frac{3}{5}$
A. $1\frac{1}{2}$ E. $1\frac{5}{9}$
M. $2\frac{3}{14}$ C. $2\frac{1}{6}$
R. $6\frac{13}{20}$ N. $3\frac{15}{22}$
T. $5\frac{5}{12}$ L. $3\frac{1}{12}$
S. $1\frac{5}{14}$ P. $1\frac{4}{9}$

WITH "EXPERI-MINTS"!

Page 65

A. $1\frac{3}{14}$ B. $1\frac{7}{22}$ C. $3\frac{5}{12}$ D. $2\frac{1}{14}$ E. $1\frac{11}{18}$
F. $2\frac{2}{9}$ G. $2\frac{13}{36}$ H. $4\frac{8}{15}$ I. $1\frac{1}{5}$ J. $\frac{11}{16}$
K. $\frac{3}{22}$ L. $1\frac{1}{10}$ M. $1\frac{1}{4}$ N. $\frac{9}{26}$ O. $2\frac{1}{6}$
P. $1\frac{4}{15}$

14	7	12	1
11	2	13	8
5	16	3	10
4	9	6	15

Page 66

Down
A. $112\frac{5}{12}$
B. 171
C. $51\frac{17}{40}$ E. $2\frac{3}{8}$ G. $1\frac{1}{4}$

Across
B. $1{,}251\frac{1}{5}$ D. $281\frac{1}{5}$ E. $20\frac{1}{3}$
F. $17\frac{3}{8}$ G. $11\frac{1}{8}$

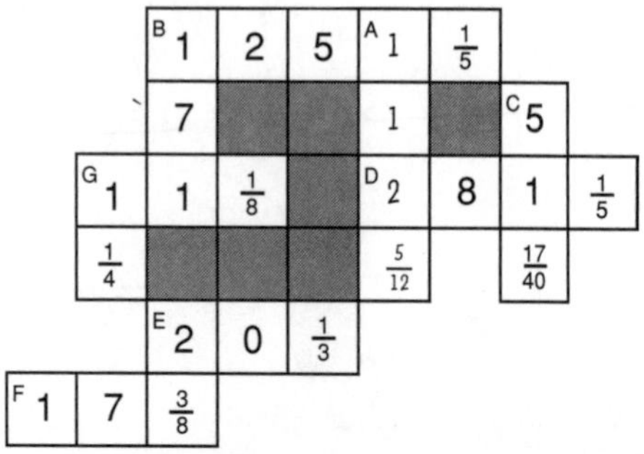

Page 67

A. $\frac{1}{2}$ B. $\frac{3}{4}$
C. $\frac{7}{8}$ D. $\frac{3}{4}$
E. $\frac{4}{5}$ F. $\frac{3}{10}$
G. $\frac{3}{5}$ H. $\frac{3}{4}$
I. $\frac{7}{9}$
J. $\frac{13}{14}$

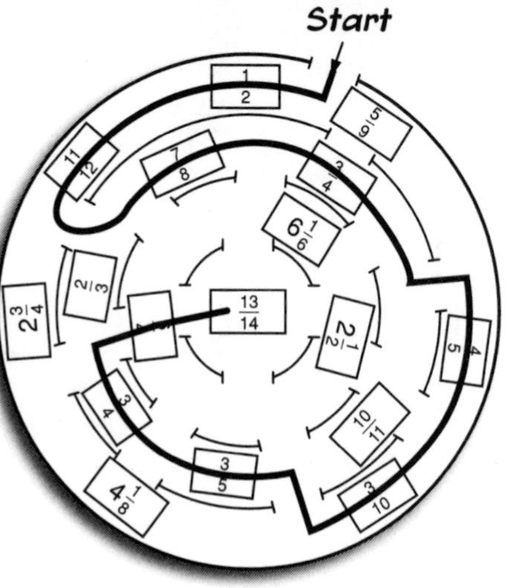

Page 68

1. $\frac{4}{5}$ 2. $2\frac{1}{3}$
3. $2\frac{1}{6}$ 4. $1\frac{2}{3}$
5. $6\frac{2}{3}$ 6. $3\frac{7}{9}$
7. $8\frac{2}{3}$ 8. $5\frac{1}{2}$
9. $9\frac{8}{9}$ 10. $\frac{1}{3}$
11. $5\frac{2}{3}$ 12. $1\frac{11}{12}$

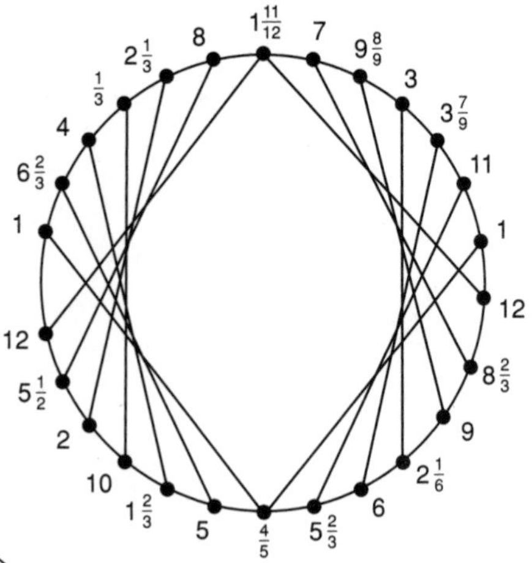

Page 69

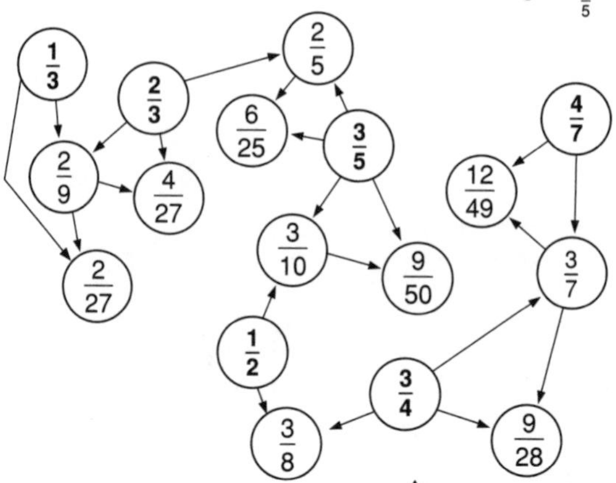

Page 70

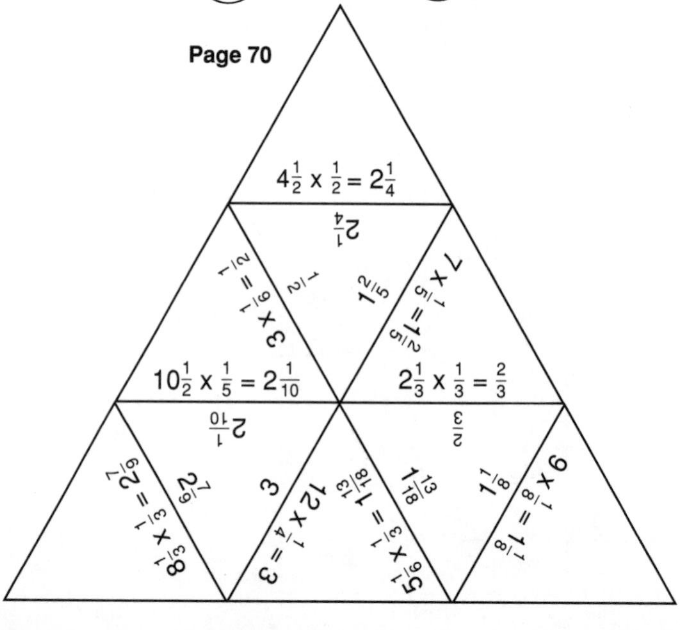

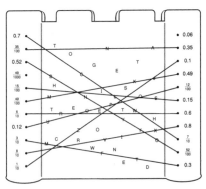

Page 71

TO GET HIS TEETH CROWNED!

Page 72

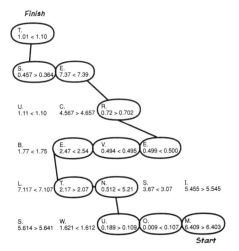

6.32	8.43	8.04 6.23
7.53	4.01 5.93	6.85
8.39	3.83 2.07	5.08
1.73	9.06 4.10	7.63

Page 73

Puzzle 1

1 in the thousandths place	1 in the hundredths place	3 in the tenths place
M	U	D
9 in the hundredths place		3 in the thousandths place
A		O
3 in the hundredths place	9 in the thousandths place	1 in the tenths place
T	U	G

Puzzle 2

5 in the hundredths place	2 in the thousandths place	7 in the tenths place
N	E	T
5 in the thousandths place		9 in the tenths place
O		A
2 in the tenths place	5 in the tenths place	2 in the hundredths place
D	I	G

Page 74

Finish

T. 1.01 < 1.10

S. 0.457 > 0.364   E. 7.37 < 7.39

U. 1.11 < 1.10   C. 4.567 < 4.657   R. 0.72 > 0.702

B. 1.77 < 1.75   E. 2.47 < 2.54   V. 0.494 < 0.495   E. 0.499 < 0.500

L. 7.117 < 7.107   T. 2.17 > 2.07   N. 0.512 < 5.21   S. 3.67 < 3.07   I. 5.455 > 5.545

S. 5.614 > 5.641   W. 1.621 < 1.612   U. 0.189 > 0.109   O. 0.009 < 0.107   M. 6.409 > 6.403

Start

MOUNT EVEREST

Page 75

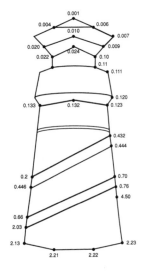

Page 76

A. 2	B. 16	
C. 13	D. 22	
E. 35	F. 5	
G. 10	H. 23	
I. 3	J. 9	
K. 12	L. 11	
M. 34	N. 15	
O. 14		

34

B 16	3	2	C 13
5	G 10	11	8
J 9	6	7	K 12
4	N 15	O 14	1

15

A 2	7	6
9	F 5	1
4	I 3	8

69

D 22	12	E 35
36	H 23	10
L 11	M 34	24

Page 77

A. 5.06
B. 11.77
C. 10.68
D. 1.78
E. 601.7
F. 0.6
G. 3.1
H. 379.2
I. 0.2
J. 21.1

6,172,882,716

Page 78

1. 97.7	2. 77.92	3. 92.59
4. 59.1	5. 91.81	6. 810.48
7. 48.28	8. 28.8	9. 88.18
10. 18.3	11. 83.456	12. 56.470

Page 79

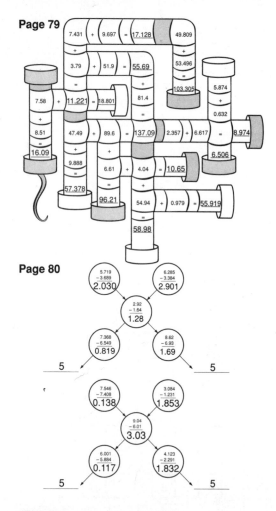

Page 80

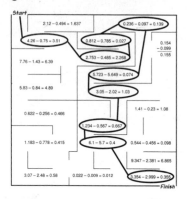

Page 81

(maze with subtraction problems)

Page 82

1.
0.05	**8**
5	0.5

2.
1.02	2
12	0.2

3.
0.02	0.6
1	3

4.
11	0.02
2	0.4

5.
10	0.3
15	0.02

6.
9	2.2
2.3	8

7.
0.21	10.5
2	4

8.
4.2	6
7	0.7

9.
5.3	7.8
3	2

Page 83

M.	1.6	W.	5.58	L.	0.496
	x 4		x 7		x 8
	6.4		39.06		3.968

E.	21.8	R.	16.43	S.	7.018
	x 9		x 5		x 6
	196.2		82.15		42.108

L.	36.2	N.	4.514
	x 2		x 2
	108.6		9.028

O. 56.18
x 6
337.08

ROSWELL, NM

Page 84

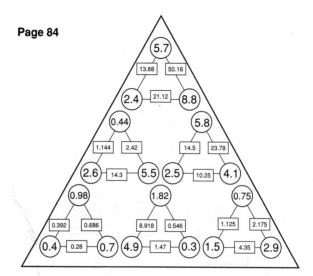

Page 85

Across	Down
A. 2.52	B. 54.81
D. 14.592	C. 4.254
F. 3.51	D. 16.56
H. 0.224	E. 24.48
J. 5.525	G. 5.769
K. 46.74	I. 45.150

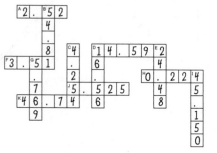

Page 86

A. 1.5	B. 1.6	C. 2.2
D. 0.3	E. 1.4	F. 2.0
G. 2.1	H. 0.7	I. 1.9
J. 0.5	K. 0.6	L. 1.8
M. 2.3	N. 0.4	O. 1.0

A 1.5	B 1.6	C 2.2	D 0.3	0.9
0.8	E 1.4	F 2.0	G 2.1	0.2
0.1	H 0.7	1.3	I 1.9	2.5
2.4	J 0.5	K 0.6	1.2	L 1.8
1.7	M 2.3	N 0.4	O 1.0	1.1